SMART SOLUTIONS

Skills, Problem Solving, Tools, and Applications

TEACHER'S RESOURCE GUIDE

Comprehensive Math Review

Pamela Halloran

New Readers Press

Acknowledgments

Advisers to the Series

Connie Eichhorn
Supervisor of Transitional Services
Omaha Public Schools
Omaha, NE

Lois Kasper
Instructional Facilitator
N.Y. Board of Education
New York, NY

Jan Phillips
Assistant Professor
William Rainey Harper College
Palatine, IL

Mary B. Puleo
Assistant Director
Sarasota County Adult and Community Education
Sarasota, FL

Margaret Rogers
Coordinator
San Juan Unified Adult Education
Sacramento, CA

ISBN 1-56420-127-9

New Readers Press
U.S. Publishing Division of Laubach Literacy International
Box 131, Syracuse, New York 13210-0131

Printed in the United States of America

Director of Acquisitions and Development: Christina Jagger
Content Editor: Mary Hutchison
Developer: Learning Unlimited, Oak Park, IL
Developmental Editor: Kathy Osmus
Copy Editor: Judi Lauber
Design: Katie Bates, Patricia A. Rapple

9 8 7 6 5 4 3 2 1

Contents

Series Overview

Math in Today's Society

Possessing solid math skills has never been more important than it is today. New technologies and the vast amount of data we encounter daily have made fundamental math skills necessary for daily living, at home, work, and school.

The ability to use number sense to make decisions and to solve problems is a critical skill in today's rapidly changing world. We are often overwhelmed by the numbers we encounter in many roles—as workers, consumers, family members, and voters. In order to function successfully, adults need to think critically and make judgments based on numbers—at work, at home, and in society at large.

Consequently, we no longer have the luxury of assuming that some people are naturally good at math but most people are not. Educators need to reexamine approaches to math education and find new ways to reach adults so they can become successful math thinkers and problem solvers.

Rethinking Math Education

Today, many teachers are looking for new directions in math teaching and learning. In part influenced by the National Council of Teachers of Mathematics (NCTM) *Curriculum and Evaluation Standards,* they are developing classrooms and looking for instructional materials and training experiences that support the goals of

- building the math self-confidence and abilities of their students
- developing students' number sense and problem-solving abilities
- demonstrating how math can improve students' personal and working lives

To accomplish these goals, teachers believe that

- **Math should be meaningful and interesting.** Curricula can be designed to engage students' interest and enhance their understanding. Through a combination of experiences, discussion, computation, and problem solving, students learn how math works.
- **Math should be practical.** In life, we carry out math with a variety of tools. We use mental math, estimation, paper and pencil, measuring instruments, and, increasingly, calculators and computers. A key goal of math instruction is acquainting students with all of these tools.
- **Math should be purposeful.** The point of a math activity should not be just doing the next math activity. Through a broad range of activities and experiences, students can apply math skills to problems and materials that they encounter in their lives.

The *Smart Solutions* Series

In keeping with these goals and characteristics, the *Smart Solutions* series consists of student material and teacher's resource guides organized around four key strands:

Skills lessons present instruction and practice with both computation and word problems.

Tools lessons provide insight into using **objects** (such as rulers or calculators) and **concepts** (such as estimation and equations) in a wide variety of situations.

Problem Solvers provide techniques to help students become successful with word problems.

Applications reflect real-life topics that require mathematics.

Five Student Books and Five Corresponding Teacher's Resource Guides

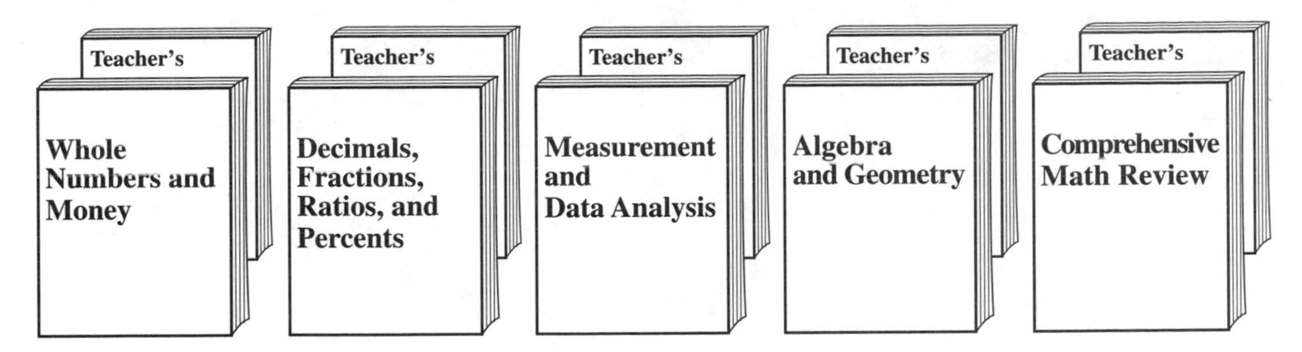

Key Features of the Student Books

Skill Preview Students can use the preview to determine the skills they already have and to decide what skills they need to concentrate on. A **Diagnostic Chart** helps to pinpoint key units and lessons that students need to study.

Unit Introduction Each unit begins with an introduction to the *skills, tools, problem solvers,* and *applications* to be covered in that unit. Each unit introduction has students think about how they use math in their lives. The **Talk About It** feature presents a discussion topic related to the contents of the unit.

Making Connections Throughout each unit, special topics invite students to connect math ideas to various interest areas and to other math concepts.

Special Problems These specially labeled problems require an in-depth exploration of math ideas. Students may be asked to **explain, draw,** find **multiple solutions,** or to do something else that demonstrates their math skills beyond "just finding an answer."

Mixed Review Periodic checkups help students see how well they understand the material. They can also gauge retention and the ability to apply skills after some time has passed.

Unit Review Cumulative reviews help students see how well they can apply the skills and concepts taught in the lessons.

Working Together At the end of each unit review, students will work with a partner or small group to apply their math skills to nonroutine problems or situations.

Posttest The posttest at the end of each book combines all of the topics taught in the book. This test is in multiple-choice format and can serve as preparation for multiple-choice standardized tests. An **Evaluation Chart** at the end of the posttest will enable you to pinpoint continuing areas of weakness.

Answer Key Students should use the answer key at the end of each book to check their work. Answers to some problems show how solutions were reached in order to help students develop their problem-solving skills.

Glossary Students should use this list of terms to learn or review key math words and ideas.

Tool Kit These resource pages at the end of each book can be used at any time.

Comprehensive Math Review

Scope and Sequence

Unit	Skills	Tools	Problem Solver	Application
1 Whole Number Review	Addition Subtraction Multiplication Division Division by Two or More Digits	Mental Math and Estimation Using Your Calculator	The Five-Step Plan	
2 Decimals and Money	Understanding Decimals Writing Decimals Comparing Decimals Adding Decimals Subtracting Decimals Multiplying Decimals Dividing Decimals	Calculators and Decimals	Solving Multistep Problems Choosing a Method	Decimals and Money Figuring Unit Price and Total Cost
3 Fractions, Ratios, and Percents	Relating Decimals and Fractions Different Forms of Fractions Equivalent Fractions Adding and Subtracting Like Fractions Finding Common Denominators Adding and Subtracting Unlike Fractions Multiplying Fractions Dividing Fractions Dividing Fractions with Mixed Numbers Relating Fractions and Ratios Writing Ratios Writing Proportions Solving Problems with Proportions Understanding Percents Decimals, Fractions, and Percents The Percent Equation Solving Percent Equations	English and Metric Rulers	Two-Step Percent Problems	Working with Distances Discounts

Comprehensive Math Review

Scope and Sequence

Unit	Skills	Tools	Problem Solver	Application
4 Data and Measurement	English Units of Length Working with Length Measuring Capacity Measuring Weight Using Metric Units Measuring Temperature Tables and Charts Bar Graphs Line Graphs Circle Graphs Scatter Diagrams Simple and Compound Probability	Using Rulers, Cups, and Spoons Reading Scales and Meters Computer Spreadsheets	Using More than One Data Source Seeing Trends, Making Predictions	Figuring Distance, Rate, and Time Mean, Median, and Mode
5 Algebra and Geometry	Writing Expressions Powers and Roots Writing Equations Order of Operations The Distributive Property Addition and Subtraction Equations Multiplication and Division Equations Writing and Solving Inequalities Points, Lines, and Angles Types of Angles Circles Quadrilaterals Triangles Similar Geometric Figures The Pythagorean Theorem Perimeter and Circumference Area Volume The Coordinate System Slope and Intercept	The Number Line Protractors	Substituting to Solve Equations Translating Words to Equations Finding Patterns in Algebra and Geometry Choosing Area, Perimeter, or Volume	Working with Formulas Reading Maps

Comprehensive Math Review
Teacher's Resource Guide

The *Teacher's Resource Guides* (*TRG*s) are key components of the *Smart Solutions* program. They provide you with guidelines for effective use of the student books.

Introduction to *Smart Solutions Teacher's Resource Guides*

The **Activity Overview** lists the student book (SB) page and the *TRG* page that correlate with each lesson activity in the unit. The Overview also lists any photocopy masters (PCMs) needed and gives the activity type for each lesson.

Unit Overviews summarize the main goals and competencies taught in each unit of the student book.

Notes about the second page of each unit help guide activities that encourage students to recognize that they already use and understand some of the skills to be covered in the lessons.

Unit 2

Decimals and Money

Activity Overview

Student Book Lesson	Pages in SB	Pages in TRG	Activity Type	PCM Number
Understanding Decimals	36	17	Hands-On	
Writing Decimals	38	17	Making Connections	4
Decimals and Money	40	18	Cooperative Learning	5
Comparing Decimals	42	18	Real-Life	
Adding Decimals	44	18	Hands-On	
Subtracting Decimals	46	19	Real-Life	6
Solving Multistep Problems	48	19	Communication	
Calculators and Decimals	52	20	Hands-On	
Multiplying Decimals	54	20	Making Connections	7
Dividing Decimals	56	21	Cooperative Learning	
Choosing a Method	58	21	Reasoning	
Figuring Unit Price and Total Cost	60	22	Real-Life/Cooperative Learning	

Unit Overview

The purpose of this unit is to give students an overall sense of the decimal system. By understanding how the decimal system works, students can apply their knowledge of basic operations to calculations with decimals. The problems in the unit demonstrate the relationships between decimals, money, and other practical applications.

When Do I Use Decimals? page 35

Remind students that decimals can be used to measure parts of a whole. Talk about the kinds of things that are measured with decimals at the workplace, at home, at retail stores, and so on. Have students read the situations at the top of the page and check the ones that apply to them. Then have students answer questions 1–3. Discuss their answers.

Talk About It page 35

Tell students that many retail stores have computers that calculate the amount of change owed to the customer. Ask students what amounts and what operation the computer uses in finding the change (cash received − total cost). Tell students that many cashiers will count back the change, starting from the total purchase cost, so customers can see that they're getting the correct change. Ask for volunteers to demonstrate this method. Encourage students to talk about how they check their change.

Working Together page 63

Have students name the sports they like to watch or play. Then list some facts and figures about the sports. Some examples are how the sports are scored, how the game is broken down (by play, by period, by total game), and what other aspects of the game are

16 *Comprehensive Math Review*

Talk About It suggests ideas for the discussion activities that open each unit.

Working Together makes suggestions for the cooperative learning activities at the end of each unit review.

Lesson-by-Lesson Notes and Classroom Activities

Lesson Title and **Page Number** from the student book are given.

Lesson Objectives for the lesson in the student book are provided.

Common Difficulties are pointed out for topics or skills that may give students difficulty as they work through the lesson in the student book.

A **Purpose** is given for each activity.

What to Do gives directions for each activity.

Substituting to Solve Equations

Problem Solver

SB p. 176

Lesson Objectives

- substitute values to solve equations
- solve an equation for one value to substitute in another equation
- substitute an expression for a variable to solve an equation
- use substitution to solve word problems

Common Difficulties

Make sure students understand which variable is the unknown being solved for. Encourage students to ask questions if this concept is unclear.

Activity

Overtime Pay

Purpose: extend the ideas in the lesson

What to Do

Show students how substitution in an equation can be used to figure total pay with overtime. Explain that businesses are required to pay hourly workers an overtime rate for hours worked over 40 hours a week. The law sets this rate at 1.5 times the regular rate (time and a half).

1. On the board, list the following: r = rate of pay, h = hours worked in 1 week, p = total weekly pay. Ask students to write an equation that could be used to find the total weekly pay for a 40-hour worker. ($40r = p$)
2. Have students use r to write an expression that shows the pay rate for the hours worked over 40 hours a week. ($1.5r$). Ask students to use h to write an expression that shows the number of hours worked over 40 in a week. ($h - 40$)
3. Help students put these expressions together to write an equation for figuring total pay with overtime. [$40r + (h - 40)(1.5r) = p$] Have students substitute values in the new equation to solve the overtime problems below. Both problems assume a 40-hour workweek and overtime pay of 1.5 times the regular rate.

- Connie worked 48 hours in 1 week and earned $624. What is Connie's regular rate of pay? ($12.00)
- Andrew worked 45 hours in 1 week. His regular pay rate is $\frac{\$9.25}{\text{hour}}$. That same week, Donna earned $40 more than Andrew. What was Donna's pay that week? ($479.40)

What to Look For

You may need to discuss why 1.5 can be used to determine overtime pay. Explain that $1\frac{1}{2}$ equals 1.5, so finding $1\frac{1}{2}$ times the regular rate is the same as multiplying the regular rate by 1.5.

Writing and Solving Inequalities

SB p. 178

Lesson Objectives

- write and solve inequalities for given situations
- graph inequalities on a number line
- use inequalities to solve word problems

Activity

Inequalities and Number Lines

Purpose: introduce the ideas in the lesson

Materials

- poster board or large piece of paper
- sales circulars from department stores

What to Do

Draw a number line on a piece of poster board. Label the line with points for –10 through 10. Circle the number 4 on the line and ask students to name some numbers that are less than 4. Explain that 4 is not a member of the set of numbers that are less than 4. Invite a volunteer to darken the number line to represent the set of all numbers that are less than 4. The circled 4 remains unshaded.

On a separate number line, color in the circle on the 4. Now ask students to name some numbers that are greater than or equal to 4. Emphasize that 4 is a member of the set of numbers because 4 is equal to 4.

Invite a volunteer to darken the number line to represent the set of all numbers that are greater than or equal to 4.

Unit 5 • Algebra and Geometry **47**

What to Look For points out possible difficulties or opportunities teachers should look for as students work through the activities in this book.

Activities are presented for each lesson.

Materials for each activity are listed so that you can prepare ahead of time. It is assumed that materials such as blackboard, chalk, paper, and pencils are always available.

Guidelines for Classroom Activities

Each *Teacher's Resource Guide* has classroom activities that foster thinking skills and problem solving with math. These activities are based on a key assumption of the NCTM *Curriculum and Evaluation Standards,* which states, "Our premise is that *what* a student learns depends to a great degree on *how* he or she has learned it." The *Standards* describes "mathematics as more than a collection of concepts and skills to be mastered; it includes methods of investigating and reasoning, means of communication, and notions of context."

To those ends, the lesson notes describe activities that foster

- Math as Communication
- Math as Reasoning
- Math as Problem Solving
- Math as Making Connections

Math as Communication

Communication is both a means and an end of mathematics learning. One means of improving students' understanding is to have them write and discuss math ideas. Students should also learn to communicate with the signs, symbols, and notations of mathematics.

Math as Reasoning

Through a variety of activities, students will make reasonable guesses, draw conclusions, and provide reasons or evidence for their thinking. This is an authentic reflection of how math is used in everyday problem solving.

Math as Problem Solving

Problem solving includes traditional word problems and much more. As with real-life math, students must solve open-ended problems and find multiple solutions.

Math as Making Connections

One of the most useful aspects of math education is making students aware of the connections among mathematical concepts and the relationship of mathematics to other content areas and to life.

Activity Techniques

In order to promote these goals, classroom techniques in the *Teacher's Resource Guides* include

- **discussion and writing** to improve students' communication with and about math ideas
- **hands-on learning** with concrete and real-life materials to encourage students to discover and manipulate math concepts
- **cooperative learning** with other students to foster group problem solving, communication, and appreciation for alternate strategies
- **calculator practice** to encourage students to use this essential math tool
- **estimation and mental math** to promote mental flexibility and comfort with numbers
- **both mathematical and real-life contexts** to help students become comfortable with both academic and authentic contexts for mathematics
- **Photocopy Masters (PCMs)** for use with the activities that follow the lesson notes in each *TRG.* Answers to problems in the PCMs are found in the Answer Key at the back of each *TRG.*

Unit 1

Whole Number Review

Activity Overview

Student Book Lesson	Pages in SB	Pages in TRG	Activity Type	PCM Number
Addition	16	12	Estimation	
Subtraction	18	12	Making Connections	
Multiplication	20	13	Real-Life	1
Division	22	13	Hands-On/Reasoning	
Division by Two or More Digits	24	14	Estimation	
Mental Math and Estimation	26	14	Real-Life/Cooperative Learning	
The Five-Step Plan	28	15	Real-Life/Cooperative Learning	2
Using Your Calculator	30	15	Hands-On	3

Unit Overview

The purpose of this unit is to review whole numbers and place value, focusing on basic operations. Students will use mental math and estimation to solve problems. The skills mastered in this unit can be applied to more complex calculations and problems involving decimals, fractions, and percents.

When Do I Use Whole Numbers? page 15

Ask students to describe experiences they have had using whole numbers. Discuss common applications for each of the four basic operations. When students have shared their experiences, ask them to check the situations at the top of the page that apply to their own lives. Then have students read through questions 1–4 and explain how they would solve each problem.

Talk About It page 15

Suggest that students think about recent school projects or household projects such as painting, cleaning, or making repairs. If necessary, provide a personal example. Discuss the importance of deadlines and of allocating ample time to meet deadlines.

Working Together page 33

In their groups, have students first examine individual estimates and determine if there are any that don't make sense. If so, they can adjust these figures before calculating the average. Discuss factors that might affect the amount of time spent watching television, such as age, workload, hobbies, school, and so on. Talk about other real-life averages that are commonly calculated. Discuss how these averages are used.

Addition

SB p. 16

Lesson Objectives

- add whole numbers, regrouping when necessary
- estimate answers to addition problems
- use addition to solve word problems

Activity

Estimation Review

Purpose: introduce the ideas in the lesson

What to Do

Most students will benefit from a review of rounding and estimation. Remind students that estimation provides an approximate answer or an answer check.

Tell students that numbers rounded to the nearest ten, hundred, or thousand are easy to work with mentally. Explain how to use the midpoints of 5, 50, and 500 to round numbers up or down. Examples:

> Round 26 to the nearest ten. Since 6 is greater than the midpoint 5, round up to 30.
>
> Round 820 to the nearest hundred. Since 20 is less than the midpoint of 50, round down to 800.
>
> Round 350 to the nearest hundred. Since 50 is equal to the midpoint, round up to 400.

On the board, write 10 or 12 two-, three-, and four-digit numbers. Have students copy the numbers and then round them to the nearest ten, hundred, or thousand. Examples: round 65 and 48 to nearest ten (70, 50); round 817 and 381 to nearest hundred (800, 400); round 1,709 and 5,432 to nearest thousand (2,000, 5,000).

After students have practiced rounding, have them work in pairs to use the rounded numbers they wrote to estimate the sums of two or more numbers. One partner selects rounded numbers to add, and the other partner estimates the sum as quickly as possible. Then partners switch roles.

Finally, have the pairs add the actual numbers and check their answers against their estimates.

Subtraction

SB p. 18

Lesson Objectives

- subtract whole numbers, regrouping when necessary
- estimate answers to subtraction problems
- use subtraction to solve word problems
- use data from a chart in solving word problems

Common Difficulties

Subtraction errors are often the result of confusion with regrouping. Students may find it helpful to use a grid to separate the digits and emphasize place value.

Activity

Subtraction Grids

Purpose: reinforce the ideas in the lesson

Materials

- graph paper

What to Do

Distribute a sheet of graph paper to each student. Have them imagine a checking account with a balance of $800. Demonstrate how to subtract a check for $42. Point out that it is sometimes necessary to regroup more than once.

	Hundreds	Tens	Ones
		9	
	7	~~10~~	10
	~~8~~	~~0~~	~~0~~
−		4	2
	7	5	8

Continue this activity. Starting with the balance of $758, students should use graph paper to subtract checks for $27, $102, $39, and $296. They should subtract each amount from the running balance. ($731, $629, $590, $294)

Have students estimate to check their work. Starting with $758 and $27, students should round amounts to the nearest ten or hundred, then subtract. The next rounded amount is then subtracted from this answer. Have students try to estimate in their heads instead of on paper.

What to Look For

Watch for the following errors:

- unnecessary regrouping (for example, mistakenly regrouping hundreds: $731 – $102 = $529)
- placement of zeros from problem to answer without subtracting (for example, bringing down the zero in the tens place without subtracting from 3: $731 – $102 = $609)

Multiplication

SB p. 20

Lesson Objectives

- multiply whole numbers, regrouping when necessary
- estimate answers to multiplication problems
- multiply by two-digit numbers
- use multiplication to solve word problems

Activity

Monthly and Yearly Budgets

Purpose: extend the ideas in the lesson

Materials

- PCM 1: Household Budgets, p. 55

What to Do

Distribute a copy of PCM 1 to each student. Explain that Budget #1 is an example of a monthly household budget. Have students use the monthly budget figures to complete an annual budget. Discuss how to change a monthly budget to a yearly budget before students begin. (Multiply each monthly expense by 12.)

After students complete the annual budget, ask questions about the various figures. Examples: *"How much money is left after monthly expenses are paid?"* ($315) *"If rent increased to five hundred dollars per month, how much more would be paid in one year?"* ($300)

Have students create their own monthly and yearly budgets on the Budget #2 work sheet. They can use rounded numbers based on their actual income and expenses or make up figures if they wish.

What to Look For

Watch for the following errors:

- improper alignment in products with two-digit multipliers
- missing zeros in products whose multipliers are multiples of 10

Division

SB p. 22

Lesson Objectives

- divide whole numbers by one-digit divisors
- use compatible numbers to estimate answers to division problems
- use division to solve word problems

Activity

Using the Remainder

Purpose: extend the ideas in the lesson

Materials

- groups of small objects that can be counted and sorted

What to Do

Explain to students that the remainder in division problems can be used in different ways, depending upon the situation.

Have students work in small groups. Give each group at least 30 objects to use as counters.

Tell students that a company plans to give each of its 28 employees a coffee mug at the annual holiday party. The manufacturer sells the mugs in 6-piece sets. Have students determine how many sets the company must buy. Tell students to put the counters in groups of 6. Ask, *"Are four groups of six enough?"* (No) *"Are five groups of six enough?"* (Yes) *"How many mugs would that be in all?"* (30) Help students understand that the company must buy

5 sets of 6 mugs, even though some mugs will be left over.

Show students how a remainder can be used to solve this problem: 28 ÷ 6 = 4 R4 (28 people divided by 6 mugs per set gives 4 sets with 4 people left over). The remainder means that if the company buys only 4 sets, 4 people will not get mugs. The company must order 5 sets and will have 2 mugs left over.

Pose some other decision-making situations and have students divide to find the numerical answers and remainders. Then discuss how the remainder is used in making the decision.

Help students to see that sometimes the remainder can be ignored and other times it will affect the final decision. Some suggestions are listed here:

- 21 chocolates for 6 people (3 chocolates per person, with 3 chocolates left over)
- number of vans needed for 16 people with 6 passengers per van (3)
- each person's share of a $29.00 gift split evenly by 3 people (one person will pay $9.66; two people will pay $9.67)

Division by Two or More Digits

SB p. 24

Lesson Objectives

- divide whole numbers by divisors of two or more digits
- estimate answers to division problems
- use data from a circle graph in solving word problems

Common Difficulties

The placement of zeros in the quotient, or answer, to a division problem can confuse students. Be prepared to provide examples of correct zero placement.

Activity

Ranges for Quotients

Purpose: reinforce the ideas in the lesson

Materials

- deck of cards with face cards removed

What to Do

Using the problem 4,785 ÷ 42, show students that there may be more than one reasonable estimate of a quotient. Have students look for compatible pairs when rounding. Round down to find a low estimate: 4,000 ÷ 40 = 100. Round the dividend up to find a high estimate: 4,800 ÷ 40 = 120.

Explain that these two sets of compatible numbers tell us that the quotient will probably be between 100 and 120.

From a deck of cards, randomly select sets of numbers to construct a division problem. For example, drawing a 10, a 5, and an 8 for the dividend and a 2 and a 9 for the divisor would result in this problem: 1,058 ÷ 29. Vary the number of digits in the dividend and divisor from problem to problem. Have students use compatible numbers to find an estimated range for the quotients.

After completing four or five problems, have students compare their estimates. Stress that there is no one correct answer.

What to Look For

As students divide, check for proper placement of digits, including zeros, in the quotient.

Mental Math and Estimation

Tools

SB p. 26

Lesson Objectives

- use front-end estimation, rounding, and compatible numbers to estimate
- understand how to decide whether an estimate or exact answer is needed

Activity

Exact or Estimate?

Purpose: reinforce the ideas in the lesson

Materials

- news articles and ads that contain numbers

What to Do

Describe some situations in which exact numbers are needed (for example, ticket price for a concert) and others in which estimates are sufficient (for example, attendance at a concert).

Bring in newspaper and magazine articles and ads that contain numbers of all sizes. You can also ask students to bring some in.

Have students work in small groups. Distribute articles and ads to each group. Have students skim the articles and discuss which numbers are estimates and which are exact. Have them give reasons for their choices.

Have small groups share their findings with the whole group.

The Five-Step Plan

Problem Solver

SB p. 28

Lesson Objective

- use the five-step plan to solve word problems

Activity

Problem Cards

Purpose: reinforce the ideas in the lesson

Materials

- PCM 2: Problem Cards, p. 56

What to Do

Have students work in pairs. Distribute a copy of PCM 2 to each pair. Have students cut out the cards and share them. One partner should have problems 1 and 2 and the answers to problems 3 and 4. The other partner should have the other four cards.

Tell students to use the five-step plan to solve their problems. Each person will need to write the answers on separate paper. When they have finished, have pairs explain their solutions to one another. The students with the answer card can point out any errors. Be sure students understand that their answers to part d will vary but should be reasonable estimates. Partners can compare solution methods to discover if there is more than one way to solve a problem.

What to Look For

Students who choose the wrong operation probably don't understand the problem. You may need to help with this part of the process, showing students how to focus on what the problem is asking.

Using Your Calculator

Tools

SB p. 30

Lesson Objectives

- understand how to read and use a calculator
- use a calculator to solve math problems

Activity

Estimate and Calculate

Purpose: reinforce the ideas in the lesson

Materials

- PCM 3: Number Grid, p. 57
- watches or clocks with second hands
- calculators

What to Do

This game will allow students to practice estimation and using a calculator. Follow these steps.

1. Group students in threes and distribute a copy of PCM 3 to each person. Make sure each group has a calculator and a watch or clock for timekeeping.
2. In each round, two players have 10 seconds to circle three numbers that have a sum close to 1,000. The third player keeps time. The timekeeper then uses the calculator to add the circled numbers. The player closest to 1,000 scores 1 point for that round.
3. After each round, numbers that have been circled on a player's sheet are crossed out and cannot be used again. Players take turns being the timekeeper.
4. Play continues until each player has been timekeeper three times. The player with the highest score wins.

Unit

2

Decimals and Money

Activity Overview

Student Book Lesson	Pages in SB	Pages in TRG	Activity Type	PCM Number
Understanding Decimals	36	17	Hands-On	
Writing Decimals	38	17	Making Connections	4
Decimals and Money	40	18	Cooperative Learning	5
Comparing Decimals	42	18	Real-Life	
Adding Decimals	44	18	Hands-On	
Subtracting Decimals	46	19	Real-Life	6
Solving Multistep Problems	48	19	Communication	
Calculators and Decimals	52	20	Hands-On	
Multiplying Decimals	54	20	Making Connections	7
Dividing Decimals	56	21	Cooperative Learning	
Choosing a Method	58	21	Reasoning	
Figuring Unit Price and Total Cost	60	22	Real-Life/Cooperative Learning	

Unit Overview

The purpose of this unit is to give students an overall sense of the decimal system. By understanding how the decimal system works, students can apply their knowledge of basic operations to calculations with decimals. The problems in the unit let students use decimals in solving money problems and other practical applications.

When Do I Use Decimals? page 35

Remind students that decimals can be used to measure parts of a whole. Talk about the kinds of things that are measured with decimals at the workplace, at home, at retail stores, and so on. Have students read the situations at the top of the page and check the ones that apply to them. Then have students answer questions 1–3. Discuss their answers.

Talk About It page 35

Tell students that many retail stores have computers that calculate the amount of change owed to the customer. Ask students what amounts and what operation the computer uses in finding the change (cash received − total cost). Tell students that many cashiers will count back the change, starting from the total purchase cost, so customers can see that they're getting the correct change. Ask for volunteers to demonstrate this method. Encourage students to talk about how they check their change.

Working Together page 63

Have students name the sports they like to watch or play. Then list some facts and figures about the sports. Some examples are how the sports are scored, how the game is broken down (by play, by period, by total game), and what other aspects of the game are recorded. Students can decide which statistics would make sense to use in comparing players, performance, or teams.

Understanding Decimals

SB p. 36

Lesson Objectives

- understand that decimals can be used to represent values less than 1
- recognize and read the place value of decimals through thousandths

Activity

Decimals and Metrics

Purpose: extend the ideas in the lesson

Materials

- centimeter rulers
- food labels or containers showing metric measures with decimals

Explain that metric measures are based on the decimal system. Metric fractional amounts are often written as decimals.

Have students work in pairs or small groups. Distribute a centimeter ruler to each group. Point out that each centimeter is divided into 10 equal parts. The smaller parts are tenths of a centimeter, or millimeters.

Explain that an object that measures 9 centimeters plus 3 smaller marks is 9 whole centimeters plus 3 tenths of a centimeter. This is written as 9.3 cm.

Have students use centimeter rulers to measure various classroom objects, then use decimals to record the measurements and explain what they mean in terms of whole and fractional amounts.

Distribute food labels to each group. Ask students to name the metric measures. Example: .946 L equals 946 thousandths of a liter. Ask students to name the digits in particular place values.

What to Look For

Students should understand that a decimal can be used to represent a part of the whole number 1. This means, for example, that the number 3.45 falls between 3 and 4. You may find it helpful to show this concept on a number line like the one shown here.

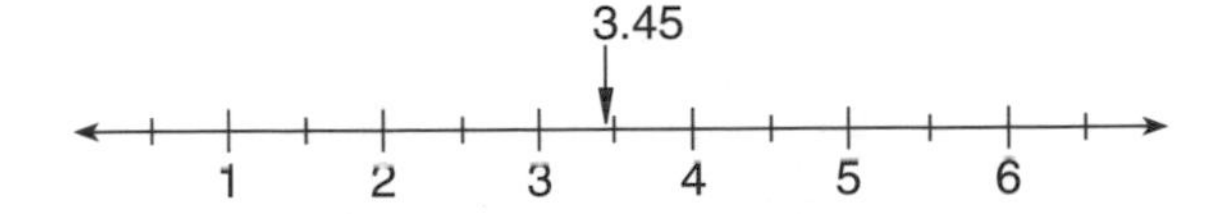

Writing Decimals

SB p. 38

Lesson Objective

- write decimals with proper placement of the decimal point and placeholder zeros

Activity

Decimal Models

Purpose: reinforce the ideas in the lesson

Materials

- PCM 4: Decimal Models, p. 57

What to Do

Distribute a copy of PCM 4 to each student. Explain that this work sheet contains two types of models that represent decimals. Each model shows the parts of a whole.

Explain that the squares are divided into 100 equal parts to represent hundredths. Point out that the 100 small squares make 1 whole larger square. The number lines have marks for tenths and marks in the middle of each tenth. Ask students what the value for these middle marks is. (5 hundredths)

Have students write the number shown by each decimal model on the line provided on the work sheet. After students complete the work sheet, have them compare answers.

As students compare their written answers, have them read the decimal numbers aloud. Emphasize that *and* or *point* are often used to indicate the separation of the whole number part and the fractional part of the decimal.

Decimals and Money

Application

SB p. 40

Lesson Objectives

- understand the relationships between the U.S. money system and decimal numbers
- write money amounts in numbers and in words

Activity

Situation Cards

Purpose: reinforce the ideas in the lesson

Materials

- PCM 5: Situation Cards, p. 58

What to Do

Have students work in pairs. Distribute a copy of PCM 5 to each pair. Then have students cut out the individual cards. Each partner should take four of the cards.

Tell students to take turns reading the situations on their cards. The partner listens and follows the instructions. The listener completes the assignment and states the answer. The reader compares that answer to the answer provided on the situation card. Discuss any differences with students.

Comparing Decimals

SB p. 42

Lesson Objectives

- use comparison symbols
- compare values of decimal amounts
- use data from a table to solve word problems

Activity

Comparing Prices

Purpose: extend the ideas in the lesson

Materials

- price lists that contain a variety of similar prices, some with dollar and cent amounts (take-out menus, newspaper ads, catalogs)

What to Do

Distribute copies of the price lists to each student. Have students compare prices on the lists. Ask questions such as, *"Which is the most expensive item on the list? Which is the least expensive item? Name five items that cost less than [name a particular item]."*

Adding Decimals

SB p. 44

Lesson Objectives

- add decimals, regrouping when necessary
- use placeholder zeros
- use a calculator to add decimals
- understand how to use the Clear Entry key on a calculator

Common Difficulties

Even students who have a solid understanding of regrouping often make errors when adding decimals because they improperly align the digits. To help students correct this tendency, have them use a grid to add decimals.

Activity

Addition Grids

Purpose: introduce the ideas in the lesson

Materials

- graph paper

What to Do

Distribute a piece of graph paper to each student. Write the following problem on the blackboard.

$$2.075 + 11.32 + 0.9$$

Tell students that because a different number of digits follow the decimal point in these numbers, it is important to align the digits carefully. Have students write 2.075 on the graph paper, putting each digit and the decimal point in a separate box. Then students should put decimal points in the next three rows directly under the first decimal point. Then have students write the remaining numbers, carefully aligning digits with the same place value. Remind students to include placeholder zeros.

Demonstrate how to add the numbers as shown below.

		1				
		2	.	0	7	5
	1	1	.	3	2	0
+		0	.	9	0	0
	1	4	.	2	9	5

For additional practice, have students write and total the following examples:

7.63 + 0.02 + 12.375 = (20.025)

15.5 + 0.14 = (15.64)

$13.97 + $2.40 + $0.98 = ($17.35)

Subtracting Decimals

SB p. 46

Lesson Objectives

- subtract decimals, regrouping when necessary
- use a calculator to subtract decimals
- use data from a table in solving word problems

Activity

Paycheck Deductions

Purpose: extend the ideas in the lesson

Materials

- PCM 6: Paycheck Deductions Work Sheets, p. 59

What to Do

Give each student a copy of PCM 6. Help students with any unfamiliar terms on the work sheet. Explain how taxes and other deductions are subtracted from gross pay to find net pay. Point out to students that the third column provides a place labeled Other for additional deductions.

Have students complete the first work sheet, using the figures given for gross pay and deductions. Students should find the total for taxes and the total for other deductions, then fill in these amounts in the first column. Students should then find the net pay by subtracting these total amounts from gross pay.

Then have students make up two samples of gross pay and deductions. Have them exchange work sheets with a partner and find the net pay.

What to Look For

When students create their own problems, they should make sure the deductions do not exceed the gross pay.

Solving Multistep Problems

Problem Solver

SB p. 48

Lesson Objectives

- describe methods for solving problems
- determine whether a problem requires one or more steps to solve
- use one or more steps to solve problems

Activity

I Have a Problem

Purpose: reinforce the ideas in the lesson

What to Do

Ask students to think about problems involving numbers and operations they have recently encountered. You might suggest some situations, such as paying a bill, cooking, shopping, working, or traveling.

Have students write a word problem based on one of the situations. Encourage them to clearly identify the question to be answered and to include all facts needed to solve the problem.

You may have students exchange problems with a partner, or you may choose several problems for the entire class to solve. Tell students to identify whether the problem is single-step or multistep and then use the five-step method to find the solution. Discuss the solution methods students used.

Calculators and Decimals

Tools

SB p. 52

Lesson Objectives

- use calculators to solve decimal problems
- round calculator decimal answers
- find the value of the remainder in a division problem

Activity

Checking with a Calculator

Purpose: extend the ideas in the lesson

Materials

- calculators

What to Do

Distribute a calculator to each student. Remind students that one use for a calculator is to check computations performed mentally or with paper and pencil. Explain that students can also check answers by using the opposite, or inverse, operation. Addition and subtraction are inverse operations.

Use the following example to demonstrate this concept:

3.5 + 6.2 = 9.7

Check: 9.7 − 6.2 *or* 9.7 − 3.5

Point out that this kind of checking can be performed easily and quickly with a calculator. Have students solve the following problems on a calculator. Students should then use a calculator to check the answers with inverse operations.

2.8 + 4.5 = (7.3)	10.2 + 4.8 = (15.0)
5.5 − 2.6 = (2.9)	7.3 − 2.2 = (5.1)
8.6 + 1.3 = (9.9)	1.7 + 6.76 = (8.46)
3.45 − 1.12 = (2.33)	6 − 4.45 = (1.55)

Multiplying Decimals

SB p. 54

Lesson Objectives

- multiply decimals by decimals and whole numbers
- understand how to use placeholder zeros when multiplying decimals
- multiply decimals by 10, 100, and 1,000
- use a calculator to solve decimal multiplication problems

Activity

What Rates?

Purpose: extend the ideas in the lesson

Materials

- PCM 7: What Rates?, p. 60
- calculators

What to Do

Explain to students that a rate is a relationship that compares an amount to a particular unit. Provide examples such as miles per hour and pay per hour or per day. Encourage students to name other familiar rates.

Tell students that rate problems often involve multiplying decimals. Model the following example.

Pay rate: $12.75 per hour

Hours worked: 32

Total pay: 32 × $12.75 = $408

Distribute a copy of PCM 7 and a calculator to each student. Allow them to use calculators in solving these rate problems.

What to Look For

If students are using calculators, they should also estimate to check their answers. You may need to lead a discussion with students about which numbers they could round to find approximate answers. Remind students that for every problem they should ask themselves if the answer makes sense.

Dividing Decimals

SB p. 56

Lesson Objectives

- divide decimals by whole numbers and decimals
- divide by 10, 100, and 1,000
- calculate averages
- use data from a table in solving word problems

Activity

Think Big

Purpose: reinforce the ideas in the lesson

Materials

- index cards or small pieces of paper
- clocks or watches with second hands
- calculators

What to Do

Have students work in pairs. Distribute 10 index cards or pieces of paper, a watch or clock, and a calculator to each pair. Each pair should make a card for each digit 0 through 9.

Tell students that they will use the digits to create division problems. The object is to create a division problem that will produce the largest quotient (answer) possible. Have students follow these steps:

1. One partner shuffles the cards and fans them facedown. The other partner pulls out five cards and uses the numbers to construct a division problem. The division problem must include one number with a hundredth decimal and one with a tenth decimal.

2. The student has one minute to construct and answer the problem. The partner keeps time. Then the partner uses a calculator to check the quotient. The first student records the quotient.

3. Partners take turns constructing and solving division problems. After five rounds, students total their quotients. The player with the greatest total wins.

Choosing a Method

Problem Solver

SB p. 58

Lesson Objectives

- understand how to use numerical expressions in solving problems
- apply the order of operations
- select the best method to solve a problem
- recognize equivalent expressions

Activity

Looking at Operations

Purpose: introduce the ideas in the lesson

Materials

- SB p. 59

What to Do

Demonstrate how to match verbal expressions with numerical expressions and apply the order of operations. Use problem 5 in Part B on student book page 59 as an example. Tell students that a builder bought 80 lighting fixtures at $39.50 each. Ask, *"What operation would you use to find the total amount spent on the lights?"* (multiplication) Then have students look at the answer choices to determine if any can be eliminated because they do not include multiplication. [Choice (2) can be eliminated.]

Next, tell students that the builder paid $252.80 in sales tax. Ask, *"What operation would be used to find the total amount spent on lights including sales tax?"* (addition) Now have students decide which answer choice can be eliminated. [Choice (1) can be eliminated.]

Have students examine the remaining choice to see if it matches the numbers and operations they named. Help students conclude that choice (3) involves multiplying the price per light by the number of lights and then adding the sales tax.

You may wish to model other problems from the exercise.

Figuring Unit Price and Total Cost

Application

SB p. 60

Lesson Objectives

- calculate unit price and total cost
- use unit prices to determine best buys
- organize information in a table to solve problems

Activity

Supermarket Prices

Purpose: reinforce the ideas in the lesson

Materials

- sales circulars from local supermarkets

What to Do

Have students work in pairs, and give each pair a supermarket sales circular. Have partners read through the flyers and calculate unit prices for various products. You can model the following example for students: 22-fl.-oz. bottle of dishwashing detergent at $.99 = $.045 per fl. oz. = 4.5¢ per fl. oz. Ask students to list their examples on a piece of paper.

Have partners read through the flyers again, this time looking for advertised unit prices. Example: grapes at $.88 per pound. Ask students to write the unit price and then figure the total cost to purchase a particular amount. You can model the following example: $.88 × 1.2 lb. grapes = $1.06.

Have students share their pricing information with the class. If possible, determine best buys for similar products.

Have students discuss what other factors, besides price, affect what is considered a best buy (e.g., amount needed, shelf life of the product, product preference, quality differences among products with different prices).

Unit 3

Fractions, Ratios, and Percents

Activity Overview

Student Book Lesson	Pages in SB	Pages in TRG	Activity Type	PCM Number
Relating Decimals and Fractions	66	24	Making Connections	8
Different Forms of Fractions	68	24	Calculator Practice	
Equivalent Fractions	70	25	Making Connections	9
English and Metric Rulers	72	25	Hands-On	
Adding and Subtracting Like Fractions	74	26	Making Connections	9
Finding Common Denominators	76	26	Real-Life	
Adding and Subtracting Unlike Fractions	78	26	Real-Life	
Working with Distances	80	27	Hands-On	
Multiplying Fractions	82	27	Hands-On	
Dividing Fractions	84	28	Hands-On	
Dividing Fractions with Mixed Numbers	86	28	Real-Life	10
Relating Fractions and Ratios	90	28	Making Connections	
Writing Ratios	92	29	Hands-On	11
Writing Proportions	94	29	Real-Life	
Solving Problems with Proportions	96	30	Hands-On	
Understanding Percents	98	30	Real-Life	12
Decimals, Fractions, and Percents	100	31	Communication	13
The Percent Equation	102	31	Cooperative Learning	
Solving Percent Equations	104	31	Real-Life	
Discounts	106	32	Real-Life/Cooperative Learning	14
Two-Step Percent Problems	108	32	Real-Life/Reasoning	

Unit Overview

The purpose of this unit is to demonstrate the relationships between fractions, ratios, percents, and decimals. Students will see that these systems can all be used to represent parts of a whole. Students will also discover that the concepts in this unit have many practical real-life applications.

When Do I Use Fractions, Ratios, and Percents? page 65

Ask students to give examples of fractions, ratios, and percents. If necessary, provide examples of ratios, for example, 3 cans of water to 1 can of juice concentrate. Then have students tell when they might use each of these types of numbers. After students have discussed fractions, ratios, and percents, ask them to check the experiences at the top of the page that apply to them. Then have students read questions 1–3 and give details for each situation.

Talk About It page 65

Tell students that one way to estimate size or distance is to compare with a familiar object or situation. Have students think of common items that measure about a foot, such as a person's foot. Continue with longer lengths or distances. For example, the distance a golf ball traveled could be estimated by comparing it to a football field, which is 100 yards divided into 10-yard segments.

Working Together page 111

To start students on this activity, encourage them to create a typical daily schedule. Suggest that they outline time periods for particular activities, such as wake up at 6:30, work 9:00 to 5:00 with 30 minutes off to eat lunch, and so on. The schedules will outline the breakdown of an average day. Then students can figure the percent of time spent on each activity in a 24-hour period to create the graph.

Relating Decimals and Fractions

SB p. 66

Lesson Objectives

- understand the relationship between fractions and decimals
- write fractions as decimals and decimals as fractions
- compare decimals and fractions
- use comparison symbols
- use data from a table in solving problems

Activity

Part and Whole Models

Purpose: introduce the ideas in the lesson

Materials

- PCM 8: Part and Whole Models, p. 61

What to Do

Distribute a copy of PCM 8 to each student. Direct attention to the first problem. Ask students how many total boxes there are in this figure. (10) Then ask how many are shaded. (3) Show students how to write the part (the number of shaded boxes) above the fraction bar and the whole (total number of boxes) below the fraction bar.

Explain that the top number, or numerator, in a fraction represents the part, while the bottom number, or denominator, represents the whole.

Remind students that the fraction in this problem can also be expressed as a decimal. Ask for a volunteer to name this decimal. (0.3)

If necessary, do the second problem with students. Have them complete the handout by writing the appropriate fractions and decimals.

Different Forms of Fractions

SB p. 68

Lesson Objectives

- understand the relationship between fractions and division
- write fractions as mixed and whole numbers and mixed numbers as fractions
- use calculators to convert fractions to decimals

Activity

Eighths and Twelfths

Purpose: extend the ideas in the lesson

Materials

- calculators

What to Do

Distribute a calculator to each student. Explain that in some situations, students may want to use a calculator to work out problems that involve fractions. Some fractions, such as halves, thirds, quarters, and fifths, are easily converted to decimals and may be memorized quickly. Eighths and twelfths are commonly used fractions that are not as easily converted and memorized.

Show students how to use a calculator to find the decimal equivalent of $\frac{1}{8}$. Explain that the bar in the fraction tells you to divide ($1 \div 8$). Instruct students to press the following keys: [1] [÷] [8] [=].

On the board, write a chart of fractions: $\frac{1}{8}$ through $\frac{7}{8}$ and $\frac{1}{12}$ through $\frac{11}{12}$. Tell students to copy this chart and then use a calculator to find and write the decimal equivalents to the thousandths place for each fraction. They should include placeholder zeros as necessary.

$\frac{1}{8}$ = (.125)	$\frac{5}{8}$ = (.625)	$\frac{1}{12}$ = (.083)	$\frac{5}{12}$ = (.417)	$\frac{9}{12}$ = (.750)
$\frac{2}{8}$ = (.250)	$\frac{6}{8}$ = (.750)	$\frac{2}{12}$ = (.167)	$\frac{6}{12}$ = (.500)	$\frac{10}{12}$ = (.833)
$\frac{3}{8}$ = (.375)	$\frac{7}{8}$ = (.875)	$\frac{3}{12}$ = (.250)	$\frac{7}{12}$ = (.583)	$\frac{11}{12}$ = (.917)
$\frac{4}{8}$ = (.500)		$\frac{4}{12}$ = (.333)	$\frac{8}{12}$ = (.667)	

You may wish to do a few of the calculations with students, showing them how to fill in the chart. Suggest that students keep the chart for reference.

Equivalent Fractions

SB p. 70

Lesson Objectives

- write equivalent fractions
- write fractions in lowest terms
- use data from a table in solving word problems

Activity

Equivalent Fraction Models

Purpose: introduce the ideas in the lesson

Materials

- PCM 9: Fraction Models, p. 62
- scissors

What to Do

Distribute a copy of PCM 9 to each student. Provide enough pairs of scissors for students to share. Have students count the number of parts in each figure and label each with the appropriate fraction name (halves, thirds, fourths, etc.).

Tell students to cut out each figure. Explain that these figures can be used to find equivalent fractions—two fractions that are equal to one another.

Have students align the figures for fourths and sixths. Have them count 2 fourths and look for a part of the sixths figure that is equal to $\frac{2}{4}$. Guide them to see that $\frac{2}{4}$ is equivalent to $\frac{3}{6}$.

Have students use the models to find other equivalent fractions, for example, $\frac{2}{3}$, $\frac{4}{6}$, and $\frac{8}{12}$; $\frac{4}{5}$ and $\frac{8}{10}$; $\frac{6}{8}$ and $\frac{3}{4}$; $\frac{4}{12}$, $\frac{2}{6}$, and $\frac{1}{3}$.

Have students study the equivalent fractions they found. Have them identify which of the fractions are in lowest terms. Then have them determine what the figures for those fractions in lowest terms have in common. (The figure for the fraction in lowest terms has the fewest parts.)

What to Look For

As students find equivalent fractions and fractions in lowest terms, make sure they represent the part with the numerator and the whole with the denominator.

English and Metric Rulers

Tools

SB p. 72

Lesson Objectives

- understand the units used on English and metric rulers
- use English and metric rulers to measure objects

Activity

Inches or Centimeters

Purpose: reinforce the ideas in the lesson

Materials

- English and metric rulers
- common classroom objects, such as books, pencils, pens, desks, and calculators

What to Do

Have students work in pairs. Distribute English and metric rulers to each pair. Make sure each pair also has several classroom objects to measure.

Have students first write an *estimate* for the measure of an object in both inches and centimeters. They should then measure the object with both English and metric rulers and write the measurements next to their estimates.

Have students repeat this process for different objects. Encourage them to vary the way they record the metric measures, for example, 54 mm, 5 cm 4 mm, or

5.4 cm. Discuss with students whether or not their estimates improved with practice.

What to Look For

Make sure students don't confuse the intermediate marks: tenths on metric and sixteenths on English rulers.

Adding and Subtracting Like Fractions

SB p. 74

Lesson Objectives

- recognize like fractions
- add and subtract like fractions
- use like fractions to solve word problems
- use data from a chart in solving word problems

Activity

Adding and Subtracting with Fraction Models

Purpose: introduce the ideas in the lesson

Materials

- PCM 9: Fraction Models, p. 62

What to Do

Distribute a copy of PCM 9 to each student. Demonstrate how to use the 4-part model to add $\frac{1}{4}$ and $\frac{2}{4}$ by first shading 1 box and then 2 boxes for a total of $\frac{3}{4}$.

Demonstrate subtraction with the problem $\frac{4}{5} - \frac{1}{5}$. Have students lightly shade 4 boxes of the 5-part model and then erase the shading in 1 box. This leaves a difference of 3 boxes, or $\frac{3}{5}$.

Use additional examples if necessary: $\frac{1}{3} + \frac{1}{3} = \left(\frac{2}{3}\right)$; $\frac{4}{6} - \frac{1}{6} = \left(\frac{3}{6}\right)$; $\frac{3}{8} + \frac{3}{8} = \left(\frac{6}{8}\right)$; $\frac{7}{10} - \frac{3}{10} = \left(\frac{4}{10}\right)$; $\frac{5}{12} + \frac{3}{12} = \left(\frac{8}{12}\right)$

Finding Common Denominators

SB p. 76

Lesson Objectives

- recognize unlike fractions
- write equivalent fractions to find common denominators

Activity

A Fraction of Time

Purpose: extend the ideas in the lesson

What to Do

Draw a clock face on the board with the numerals 1–12 evenly spaced. Tell students that time is often expressed in fractions of an hour. Time spent on jobs or other activities can be recorded in hours and fractions of an hour. Invite students to describe other time situations that can be broken down this way.

Have students find the fractional part of an hour for each 5-minute increment from 5 to 60 minutes. Provide this example: *"An hour equals sixty minutes, so five minutes is five sixtieths, or one twelfth, of an hour."* Ask students to write each increment in minutes and then as a fraction of an hour. For example, 15 minutes is $\frac{1}{4}$ or one quarter of an hour, as in the phrase "quarter after five." (Other answers: 10 minutes is $\frac{1}{6}$ hour; 20 minutes is $\frac{1}{3}$ hour; 25 minutes is $\frac{5}{12}$ hour; 30 minutes is $\frac{1}{2}$ hour; 35 minutes is $\frac{7}{12}$ hour; 40 minutes is $\frac{2}{3}$ hour; 45 minutes is $\frac{3}{4}$ hour; 50 minutes is $\frac{5}{6}$ hour; 55 minutes is $\frac{11}{12}$ hour; 60 minutes is 1 hour.)

Name various activities and the time needed to complete them. Have students express the time in hours and fractions of an hour. You may use the examples below.

ate breakfast 7:15–8:00 $\left(\frac{3}{4}\text{ hour}\right)$; drove 2:40–3:10 $\left(\frac{1}{2}\text{ hour}\right)$; mowed lawn 9:30–11:10 ($1\frac{2}{3}$ hours)

Adding and Subtracting Unlike Fractions

SB p. 78

Lesson Objectives

- change unlike fractions to like fractions
- add and subtract unlike fractions

Activity

Study Time

Purpose: extend the ideas in the lesson

What to Do

Remind students that time can be expressed in hours and fractions of an hour.

Have students form pairs or small groups. List the times below on the board.

Monday—1:30–2:15

Tuesday—4:20–5:10

Wednesday—2:45–3:45

Thursday—3:45–4:30

Friday—8:00–8:40

Then pose this problem. *"For a week, Daniel tracked his math studying time. Find the time Daniel spent each day studying math. Write your answers in fraction form."*

Then have students write problems that require adding and subtracting fractions and exchange their problems with other pairs or groups to solve. Sample problems are "How much time did he spend studying Monday and Tuesday?" ($1\frac{7}{12}$ hours) "How much more time did he spend studying on Wednesday than on Thursday?" $\left(\frac{1}{4}\text{ hour}\right)$ "How much time did he spend all week studying?" (4 hours)

What to Look For

As students find equivalent fractions, be sure they multiply both the numerator and denominator by the same number.

Working with Distances

Application

SB p. 80

Lesson Objectives

- add and subtract fractions and mixed numbers to calculate distances
- use distances marked on a map in solving word problems

Activity

Flick the Coin

Purpose: reinforce the ideas in the lesson

Materials

- coins and masking tape
- rulers, yardsticks, or tape measures

What to Do

This game will give students practice measuring with rulers and calculating distances.

Have students form groups of three or four, and give each group member a coin of the same denomination. Distribute tape and rulers, yardsticks, or tape measures to each group. Have students write their initials on a small piece of tape and label their coins. Then have them place a piece of masking tape on the floor to mark the start line. Each member of the group has a turn flicking a coin. The object is to see who can flick a coin the farthest.

When all players in a group have flicked their coins, students measure the distance from the start line to each coin and record it. Suggest that groups play two or three rounds. At the end of all the rounds, players should add their own distances to get a total for each player. Within their group, students then subtract to find the difference between the first-place (greatest) distance and the second-place distance, and between the second-place distance and the third-place distance. Then groups can compare their results.

Multiplying Fractions

SB p. 82

Lesson Objective

- multiply fractions by fractions

Activity

Multiplication Models

Purpose: introduce the ideas in the lesson

Materials

- graph paper

What to Do

Multiplying a fraction by a fraction gives an answer smaller than either of the original fractions. (*Note:* This is not true of improper fractions.) In this activity, students discover visually why this is so.

Distribute a piece of graph paper to each student. Tell students to outline a 4×4 grid on the graph paper and then shade $\frac{1}{2}$ of this grid. Then have students darken $\frac{1}{2}$ of the $\frac{1}{2}$ they just shaded. They should see that the result, $\frac{1}{4}$, is smaller than the original fractions, $\frac{1}{2}$ and $\frac{1}{2}$. Have students write out the problem they just demonstrated: $\frac{1}{2} \times \frac{1}{2} = \frac{1}{4}$.

You may wish to have students demonstrate other problems, such as $\frac{1}{4} \times \frac{3}{4} \left(= \frac{3}{16}\right)$ with a 16×16 grid or $\frac{1}{3} \times \frac{1}{2} \left(= \frac{1}{6}\right)$ with a 1×6 grid.

Dividing Fractions

SB p. 84

Lesson Objectives

- divide fractions by fractions and whole numbers
- estimate with fractions, rounding to $\frac{1}{2}$ or 1

Activity

Division and Multiplication

Purpose: introduce the ideas in the lesson

What to Do

Explain to students that to divide by a fraction, they invert that fraction and multiply.

On the board, write the problem $4 \div \frac{1}{2}$. Tell students that this problem asks the question, "How many halves are in four?"

Draw four squares on the board and divide each in half. Use this model to show that there are 8 halves in 4. Write the following number sentences:

$$4 \div \frac{1}{2} = 8$$
$$4 \times \frac{2}{1} = 4 \times 2 = 8.$$

Remind students that 2 is $\frac{1}{2}$ inverted. Have students find the product $2 \times \frac{1}{2}$ (1). Tell students that any two numbers with a product of 1 are called reciprocals. To divide by a fraction, you multiply by its reciprocal.

Have students draw figures to demonstrate the problems below. Then have them use reciprocals to write a number sentence for each figure.

$$2 \div \frac{1}{2} = (2 \times \frac{2}{1} = 4)$$
$$\frac{1}{4} \div 2 = \left(\frac{1}{4} \times \frac{1}{2} = \frac{1}{8}\right)$$

Dividing Fractions with Mixed Numbers

SB p. 86

Lesson Objectives

- divide fractions and mixed numbers
- estimate answers to division problems with mixed numbers

Common Difficulties

As students divide by mixed numbers, check that they remember to convert the mixed number to an improper fraction, then invert the fraction.

Activity

Mixed Nuts

Purpose: reinforce the ideas in the lesson

Materials

- PCM 10: Mixed Nuts, p. 63

What to Do

Distribute a copy of PCM 10 to each student. Have them complete the handout to practice dividing with fractions and mixed numbers.

Relating Fractions and Ratios

SB p. 90

Lesson Objectives

- understand the relationship between fractions and ratios
- express ratios in different forms
- express ratios in lowest terms

Activity

Class Ratios

Purpose: introduce the ideas in the lesson

What to Do

To introduce the idea of a ratio, have students count the number of men, the number of women, and the total number of people in the class.

Explain that these numbers can be compared in different ways: number of men to total number of people, number of women to total number of people, number of men to number of women, and number of women to number of men. Write these ratios and show how to simplify them to lowest terms.

Continue with other examples, such as hair color and eye color.

Writing Ratios

SB p. 92

Lesson Objectives

- write ratios for different situations
- convert units to write ratios
- use data from tables in writing ratios

Activity

Class Questionnaire

Purpose: reinforce the ideas in the lesson

Materials

- PCM 11: Class Questionnaire, p. 64
- scissors

What to Do

Distribute a copy of PCM 11 to each student. Provide enough pairs of scissors for students to share. After students complete the questionnaire, have them cut off part A. Collect the questionnaires.

On the board, keep a tally of the answers to each question. Have students use the tallied results to write the ratios described in part B of PCM 11.

When students have completed the handout, ask them to think of another ratio that can be written for each question in the questionnaire. They can then work with a partner to find these additional ratios.

What to Look For

As students write ratios, check to see that the order of the numbers is correct.

Writing Proportions

SB p. 94

Lesson Objectives

- understand that a proportion is two equal ratios or equivalent fractions
- use cross products to determine if two ratios are equal
- use cross products and equations to find missing numbers
- make a table to solve proportion problems

Activity

Reference Table

Purpose: extend the ideas in the lesson

What to Do

Tell students that ratios presented in a table format are often easy-to-use sources of information.

Have students imagine that they run a catering service. The service caters events for groups of different sizes. When planning an event, the catering service figures the amount of food needed based on groups of 10 people. For example, to provide appetizers for 10 people the service would need 1 lb. (16 oz.) of dip, $2\frac{1}{4}$ lb. of shrimp, and $1\frac{1}{2}$ lb. of cheese.

As a group, use this information to make a table for the catering business (see the table below). On the board, draw and label the table. Fill in the amounts for 10 people. Ask students to calculate the amounts for 20, 30, 40, and 50 people.

Number of People	10	20	30	40	50
Amount of Dip	1 lb.	(2 lb.)	(3 lb.)	(4 lb.)	(5 lb.)
Amount of Shrimp	$2\frac{1}{4}$ lb.	($4\frac{1}{2}$ lb.)	($6\frac{3}{4}$ lb.)	(9 lb.)	($11\frac{1}{4}$ lb.)
Amount of Cheese	$1\frac{1}{2}$ lb.	(3 lb.)	($4\frac{1}{2}$ lb.)	(6 lb.)	($7\frac{1}{2}$ lb.)

Solving Problems with Proportions

SB p. 96

Lesson Objectives

- use proportions to solve problems
- use data from a chart in solving proportion problems

Activity

Scale Drawings

Purpose: extend the ideas in the lesson

Materials

- English rulers or tape measures and metric rulers
- graph paper

What to Do

Discuss the use of scale drawings for such things as construction projects and interior design. Explain how the objects in the drawing are proportional to the actual objects.

Demonstrate how to use a scale. On the board, write 12 in. = 2 cm. Show how to find the actual size of an item represented on a scale drawing by solving a proportion. Use this as an example:

$$\frac{2 \text{ cm}}{12 \text{ in.}} = \frac{5 \text{ cm}}{x \text{ in.}}$$

$$2x = 60$$

$$x = 30 \text{ in.}$$

Have students work in pairs. Distribute graph paper and rulers to each pair. Have them use a scale of 12 in. = 2 squares to make a scale drawing of an object in the classroom. Suggest items that are easy to draw, such as a table or desk top, a blackboard, a window, and so on. Students should first measure the object, then use the scale and proportion to find the dimensions necessary to make a scale drawing.

What to Look For

When students set up their proportions, check that both ratios are in the same order.

Understanding Percents

SB p. 98

Lesson Objectives

- understand the meaning of percents
- relate percents to the whole (100%)
- use data from a table in calculating percents

Activity

Percents and Vitamins

Purpose: extend the ideas in the lesson

Materials

- PCM 12: Percents and Vitamins, p. 65

What to Do

Distribute a copy of PCM 12 to each student. Ask for volunteers to tell what they know about the recommended daily allowance (RDA) for vitamins and minerals. For example, students may have noticed the nutrition labels on food. The label says what percent of the RDA of vitamins and minerals are provided in a serving of that particular product. The daily percent of fat, cholesterol, and carbohydrates are often listed as well. This information is based on a 2,000-calorie diet.

Tell students that the table on PCM 12 shows the percent of the RDA for Vitamins A and C in one serving of certain vegetables. Point out that 100% represents the RDA. Have students use the information in the chart to solve the problems on the handout.

Discuss with students which vegetables in the chart they prefer. Then have them determine whether each serving of their preferences provides more or less than 50% of the RDA for Vitamins A and C.

Decimals, Fractions, and Percents

SB p. 100

Lesson Objectives

- understand the relationships between decimals, fractions, and percents
- convert between percents and decimals
- convert between fractions and decimals
- create a chart of common equivalent fractions, percents, and decimals

Activity

Express Yourself!

Purpose: reinforce the ideas in the lesson

Materials

- PCM 13: Express Yourself!, p. 66
- scissors

What to Do

Have students work in pairs. Distribute a copy of PCM 13 and a pair of scissors to each pair. Have them follow these steps.

1. Cut out the individual cards. Share the cards so each student has four cards.
2. Pairs should alternate reading the statements on their cards to each other. The listener must write a similar statement using the different form mentioned on the card.
3. Students then check their statements against the answers on their partners' cards.

The Percent Equation

SB p. 102

Lesson Objectives

- write percent statements
- change percent statements to percent equations
- read data from a circle graph

Activity

Percents on Food Labels

Purpose: reinforce the ideas in the lesson

Materials

- nutrition labels from various food items

What to Do

Bring in nutrition labels from various types of food. Have students work in small groups. Give each group two or three labels. Each group should write six different percent problems using the information on the labels. They should also write the problems in equation form.

Model the activity for students. Say, *"Suppose ten of two hundred ten total calories are from fat. What is the percent of calories from fat in this food? x percent of two hundred ten equals ten."*

Encourage them to vary the percent equations as shown in the lesson (% of a given number, % of unknown number = given number, and what % a number is of another number).

Collect the problems and equations written by each group. Save them for the next activity.

What to Look For

Students may incorrectly identify the missing part of the equation. Suggest that they focus on the question to determine what information is needed.

Solving Percent Equations

SB p. 104

Lesson Objectives

- solve percent equations to find the percent, whole, or part
- use percent equations to solve word problems
- use data from a circle graph in solving percent problems
- create a circle graph showing monthly expenses

Common Difficulties

Students may need to review solving equations when the variable is not already alone on one side.

Activity

Solving Equations

Purpose: reinforce the ideas in the lesson

Materials

- percent problems and equations students wrote for previous activity

What to Do

Select some of the percent problems and equations generated in the previous activity. Have students solve the equations individually and then compare and discuss results.

Discounts

Application

SB p. 106

Lesson Objectives

- calculate discounted price and reduction in price for percent discounts
- use two methods to calculate discounted prices
- use a calculator to find discounted prices

Activity

Deal a Discount

Purpose: reinforce the ideas in the lesson

Materials

- PCM 14: Deal a Discount, p. 67
- sales circulars from department stores
- calculators
- scissors

What to Do

Have students work in groups of three or four. Give each group two or three sales circulars, a calculator, a pair of scissors, and a copy of PCM 14. Have each group cut out the cards on the PCM and stack them.

Students take turns selecting a card at random from the pile and reading the discount information. They then select an item from one of the flyers and apply the discount described on the card to that item. They may use calculators. Have the group check each member's answers.

Two-Step Percent Problems

Problem Solver

SB p. 108

Lesson Objectives

- solve two-step percent problems
- use data from a table in solving percent problems

Activity

Computing Sales Tax

Purpose: extend the ideas in the lesson

Materials

- calculators

What to Do

Make sure each student has a calculator. Show students how to use a calculator to find total price with sales tax in one step. Use a 6% sales tax rate as an example. Tell students to multiply the price $45.80 by 1.06. Help them to understand that this is same as multiplying the price by 0.06 and adding this tax amount to the original price. Invite volunteers to explain why this method makes sense.

Have students practice this method with the tax table in the lesson. Give the prices listed below, and have students figure total price with tax for each city in the table.

Price	Danville	Frankfort	Villa Park	Yorktown
126.90	(137.37)	(134.83)	(137.05)	(136.73)
89.52	(96.91)	(95.12)	(96.68)	(96.46)
12.85	(13.91)	(13.65)	(13.88)	(13.85)
66.40	(71.88)	(70.55)	(71.71)	(71.55)

Data and Measurement

Activity Overview

Student Book Lesson	Pages in SB	Pages in TRG	Activity Type	PCM Number
English Units of Length	114	34	Hands-On	
Working with Length	116	34	Hands-On	
Measuring Capacity	118	35	Hands-On	
Using Rulers, Cups, and Spoons	120	35	Real-Life	
Measuring Weight	122	35	Real-Life/Making Connections	
Using Metric Units	124	36	Hands-On	
Measuring Temperature	126	36	Making Connections	
Reading Scales and Meters	128	37	Real-Life	15
Figuring Distance, Rate, and Time	130	37	Making Connections	
Tables and Charts	134	37	Cooperative Learning	16
Computer Spreadsheets	136	38	Real-Life	17
Bar Graphs	138	38	Hands-On	16
Line Graphs	140	38	Hands-On	18
Circle Graphs	142	39	Hands-On	19
Scatter Diagrams	144	39	Cooperative Learning	
Using More than One Data Source	146	40	Making Connections	20
Simple and Compound Probability	148	40	Hands-On	
Seeing Trends, Making Predictions	150	41	Cooperative Learning	21
Mean, Median, and Mode	152	41	Cooperative Learning	

Unit Overview

The purpose of this unit is to introduce and provide practice in different ways of working with numerical data. Students will read measurements of length, weight, capacity, temperature, and speed and will calculate with units of length, weight, and capacity. They will learn how to create and read graphs and tables and how to analyze data. Students will also become familiar with simple and compound probability and with using data in making predictions.

When Do I Measure and Use Data?

page 113

Ask students to name some items that they have recently measured and then describe how they made the measurement. Discuss the different kinds of measures (length, weight, capacity) and possible reasons for making these measurements. After students have discussed measures, ask them to check the experiences with data and measurement that apply to them. Then have students read through questions 1–4 and describe these experiences with data and measurement.

Talk About It page 113

Have students look closely at Blake's individual grades, and tell in what interval of 10 each one falls (80–89, 90–99, etc.). Ask if students think that a *B* is a reasonable grade for Blake. Encourage them to suggest other ways to find an average grade in this situation. Invite students to describe similar situations they may have experienced.

Working Together page 155

As students prepare for the survey, suggest that they think about the population that will be polled. What age groups will be included? What ethnic backgrounds are represented in the population? Answers to these questions will help students select a topic and prepare appropriate questions for the survey.

English Units of Length

SB p. 114

Lesson Objectives

- understand English units of length
- convert English units of length to larger and smaller units

Activity

Going to Any Length

Purpose: reinforce the ideas in the lesson

What to Do

To give students practice converting measurements, tell them to write their height in feet and inches. Have them convert this measurement to inches and then to yards.

Follow the same process with other known measurements, such as distance between home and work or between home and school. Students can convert from miles to yards and feet.

What to Look For

Students may be confused about when to multiply and when to divide. Emphasize that multiplication is used to convert from larger to smaller units and that division is used to convert from smaller to larger units.

Working with Length

SB p. 116

Lesson Objectives

- add, subtract, multiply, and divide English units of length, regrouping when necessary
- estimate answers before calculating
- solve word problems that involve English units of length

Common Difficulties

Remind students that regrouping with English measures differs from regrouping with metric measures. For example, since feet are divided into 12 inches, not 10, 6 ft. 4 in. regroups to 5 ft. 16 in., not 5 ft. 14 in.

Activity

Within Walking Distance

Purpose: reinforce the ideas in the lesson

Materials

- rulers, yardsticks, or tape measures
- masking tape

What to Do

Have students work in pairs to measure the length of one another's steps. Give masking tape and rulers, yardsticks, or tape measures to each pair. Students place a piece of tape on the floor as a starting point. One student stands behind the tape and then takes a step. The other student marks the length of the step by putting tape on the floor by the tips of the toes. Each student has 4 steps marked, using the end of the previous step as the start of the next step.

When partners have finished marking each other's steps, give them the following instructions.

1. Measure and record the length of each step.
2. Add the distance covered in the four steps.
3. Subtract to find the difference between the longest and shortest steps.

4. Find the average length of a step. If students need to review how to find an average, refer them to problems 4 and 5 on page 57 of the student book.

5. Use the average length to estimate how many steps it will take to walk from one point to another: across the room, from the blackboard to the door, from a desk to the door. Encourage students to test their estimates by counting the actual number of steps it takes to get from one place to another.

Measuring Capacity

SB p. 118

Lesson Objectives

- understand English units of capacity
- convert English units of capacity to larger and smaller units
- add and subtract English units of capacity
- estimate before calculating
- solve word problems that involve English units of capacity

Activity

What's the Capacity?

Purpose: reinforce the ideas in the lesson

Materials

- containers of different sizes with labels for capacity (salad dressings, sauces, oil, juice, milk, carbonated beverages)

What to Do

Ask students to bring in some containers to help with this activity. Their recyclables would be a good source for these materials.

Have students convert the measurements on the labels to different units. (64-fluid-ounce juice carton = $\frac{1}{2}$ gallon = 2 quarts = 4 pints = 8 cups)

Use the labels to pose problems. *"A full bottle of olive oil is twenty-five and one half fluid ounces. You use one cup of oil in a recipe. How many fluid ounces of oil remain in the bottle?"* ($17\frac{1}{2}$ fl. oz.)

Have students use the measurements from the labels to make up their own problems. Have each student exchange problems with a partner to solve.

Using Rulers, Cups, and Spoons

Tools

SB p. 120

Lesson Objectives

- read an English ruler
- calculate distances in English units
- understand how to measure with English measuring cups and spoons
- solve word problems that involve English measuring cups and spoons

Common Difficulties

Students may need to review the section in unit 3 on regrouping when subtracting mixed numbers.

Activity

Recipe Problems

Purpose: reinforce the ideas in the lesson

Materials

- recipes supplied by students

What to Do

Ask each student to bring in a recipe for a favorite dish. Have students write two or three problems based on the recipe. The problems might involve increasing or decreasing the recipe or converting among measurements (cups, fluid ounces, tablespoons, and teaspoons).

Students then exchange problems with a partner and then solve the problems.

Measuring Weight

SB p. 122

Lesson Objectives

- understand English units of weight
- convert English units of weight to larger and smaller units

- add and subtract English units of weight
- estimate before calculating
- solve word problems that involve English units of weight

Activity

Weight, Please

Purpose: reinforce the ideas in the lesson

Materials

- sales circulars from supermarkets

What to Do

Have students work in pairs. Give each pair a supermarket sales circular. Tell students to find examples of different units of weight.

Have students convert the weights to other units, for example, a 12-ounce package of chicken nuggets = $\frac{3}{4}$ pound.

Students can also add and subtract weights from the ad. Tell them to determine the weight of a grocery bag that contains a few items, such as a $2\frac{1}{2}$-pound bag of apples and a $14\frac{1}{2}$-ounce box of crackers ($54\frac{1}{2}$ ounces, or 3 pounds $6\frac{1}{2}$ ounces). Have students list several items, along with their weights, and then try to distribute the items between two bags so that the weight of each bag is approximately the same.

What to Look For

Make sure students don't confuse units of capacity (8 fluid ounces equals 1 cup) with units of weight (16 ounces equals 1 pound).

Using Metric Units

SB p. 124

Lesson Objectives

- become familiar with metric units of length, weight, and capacity
- convert metric units to larger and smaller units

Activity

Another Size, Another Unit

Purpose: apply the ideas in the lesson

Materials

- containers or labels showing metric measurements of various kinds

What to Do

Have students bring in containers or labels that show metric measurements. You can also bring in a few containers to provide additional practice. Have students convert the metric measurements on the labels to the next smaller or larger unit.

Measuring Temperature

SB p. 126

Lesson Objectives

- read a thermometer with Fahrenheit and Celsius scales
- become familiar with typical readings on a weather thermometer
- calculate differences in temperature

Activity

Highs and Lows

Purpose: extend the ideas in the lesson

Materials

- weather page from Sunday newspaper with high and low temperatures for various cities

What to Do

Using the daily high and low temperatures from the newspaper weather page, have students determine temperature ranges. Ask students to find the variation in daily temperatures for different cities. Ask, *"In what parts of the country do temperatures have the widest ranges? The narrowest ranges?"*

Students can also find the difference between high or low temperatures in two cities.

Reading Scales and Meters

Tools

SB p. 128

Lesson Objective

- read pound scales, speedometers, and odometers

Common Difficulties

Students may confuse the English and metric measures of miles per hour and kilometers per hour. It may be helpful to point out that a mile is close to $1\frac{1}{2}$ times the distance of a kilometer. This means that a kilometers per hour figure will always be higher than an equivalent miles per hour figure.

Activity

Speeds and Weights

Purpose: reinforce the ideas in the lesson

Materials

- PCM 15: Speeds and Weights, p. 68

What to Do

Distribute a copy of PCM 15 to each student. Tell them to read each situation and then mark the appropriate measure on the scale, speedometer, or odometer. Students should label the plotted weights and speeds with the matching letter.

Figuring Distance, Rate, and Time

Application

SB p. 130

Lesson Objectives

- use the formulas for distance, rate, and time
- solve word problems that involve distance, rate, and time

Activity

Heart Rates

Purpose: extend the ideas in the lesson

Materials

- a clock or watch with a second hand

What to Do

Help students explore another type of rate—their heart rate. Have students locate their pulse by placing two fingers at the side of their throat. Time students as they count the number of beats in 10 seconds. Have them record this heart rate.

Ask students to work in pairs. Have them jog in place or walk briskly for two or three minutes. When they have finished exercising, have students take their pulse again, counting the number of beats in 10 seconds. Compare the heart rates before and after exercising. Tell students to keep the information they collected for use in the next activity.

Tables and Charts

SB p. 134

Lesson Objectives

- read tables and charts
- use data from tables and charts to answer questions

Activity

Making Charts

Purpose: extend the ideas in the lesson

Materials

- PCM 16: Organize Data in a Chart, p. 69
- heart rate data from previous activity

What to Do

Have students work in groups of four or five, and ask them to take out their heart-rate data from the previous activity.

Distribute a copy of PCM 16 to each group. Tell students that this handout will guide them in creating a chart. Students should record their answers to problems 1–3 in the chart. Then have them use the completed table to answer the questions in problem 4.

Have students save the completed handouts for a later activity.

Computer Spreadsheets

Tools

SB p. 136

Lesson Objectives

- read and understand components of computer spreadsheets
- use data from computer spreadsheets to solve problems
- write formulas and calculate amounts to complete computer spreadsheets

Activity

Design a Spreadsheet

Purpose: reinforce the ideas in the lesson

Materials

- PCM 17: Design a Spreadsheet, p. 70

What to Do

Distribute a copy of PCM 17 to each student. Explain that salespeople are often paid a commission —a percentage of the total sales they make. The higher the sales figures, the higher the commissions.

Have students use what they have learned in this lesson to design computer spreadsheets as described on the handout.

When students have completed the handout, they can share the spreadsheets they designed in part B. Ask volunteers to present their spreadsheets to the class. Compare the column labels, the organization of data, and the payments calculated for each salesperson.

What to Look For

Make sure students don't confuse the elements of a spreadsheet. Emphasize that the cell address is a label used to identify an individual block of information. Each cell address corresponds to a piece of data.

Bar Graphs

SB p. 138

Lesson Objectives

- find information on a bar graph
- use data from a bar graph to solve problems
- draw a bar graph

Activity

Make a Double Bar Graph

Purpose: reinforce the ideas in the lesson

Materials

- completed copies of PCM 16 from Making Charts activity
- graph paper

What to Do

Have students work in the same groups as for the Making Charts activity on page 37. Distribute graph paper to each group, and have them take out their completed copies of PCM 16. Tell students that the heart rates for the group before and after exercising can be displayed on a double bar graph.

Students should determine appropriate unit labels for one of the graph's axes by finding the highest and lowest values to be plotted. Help students decide on all necessary titles and labels. Then have them plot the data on their bar graphs.

What to Look For

Make sure students provide a key to differentiate between the before and after bars on their double bar graph.

Line Graphs

SB p. 140

Lesson Objectives

- find information on a line graph
- use data from a line graph to solve problems

Activity

Grid Drawings

Purpose: introduce the ideas in the lesson

Materials

- PCM 18: Grid Drawings, p. 71

What to Do

Locating points across two axes is useful for reading line graphs and for solving problems in algebra and coordinate geometry. This exercise will introduce the concept and allow students to practice the skill.

Distribute a copy of PCM 18 to each student. Demonstrate how to locate the point D4 by reading across the horizontal axis and up the vertical axis. Name the following coordinates and have students mark these points on the first grid: D4, B5, A7, B9, D10, F9, G7, F5.

After students have plotted the points, have them connect the points with straight lines. Plot and connect the points on your own copy of PCM 18 to use as an answer key. Students who plot the points correctly will find they have drawn an octagon on the grid. For additional practice, have students draw their own figures on the second grid and then dictate the points to a partner, who reproduces the figure.

What to Look For

If students have trouble reading across and up and down on the axes, suggest that they use rulers or other straightedges.

Circle Graphs

SB p. 142

Lesson Objectives

- find information on a circle graph
- use data from a circle graph to solve problems
- create a circle graph

Activity

Dream Vacation

Purpose: reinforce the ideas in the lesson

Materials

- PCM 19: Dream Vacation, p. 72

What to Do

Distribute a copy of PCM 19 to each student.

Tell students: *"You have each won an all-expenses-paid vacation. You can go to one of the following places: the beach, the mountains, a lake, a city, a historical site, or a theme park. Which will you choose?"*

Count the number of students who raise their hands for each choice and record the results on the board. Have students record the results in the Number of Students column on the PCM. Also count and record the total number of students in the class.

In the column labeled Fraction of Total, students should write the number of students for each destination over the total number of responses.

These fractions can be expressed as percents to fill in the Percent of Total column. You may want to have students round the amounts to make the numbers easier to work with.

Students then create a circle graph to represent the group's choices. Point out that the circle is divided into eighths. Ask, *"What percent is equal to one eighth?"* (12.5%) Students can use this percent to approximate each portion of the graph. For example, 10% would be a little less than 12.5%, or $\frac{1}{8}$, of the circle graph.

Finally, have volunteers read the statements they wrote to describe their circle graphs. Discuss the statements.

What to Look For

If rounded amounts were used, be sure that the total does not exceed 100%. You may also need to review changing fractions to percents in "Decimals, Fractions, and Percents" in unit 3.

Scatter Diagrams

SB p. 144

Lesson Objectives

- read a scatter diagram
- use data from a scatter diagram to solve problems

- complete a scatter diagram
- choose an appropriate graph to represent a given situation

Activity

Height and Shoe Size

Materials

- graph paper

Purpose: reinforce the ideas in the lesson

What to Do

Make sure students understand that scatter diagrams show two characteristics of one item to determine trends and relationships between these characteristics.

Divide the class into two groups, males and females. Have each person state his or her shoe size and height in inches. Students should record the information.

Distribute graph paper to both groups. Have each group create a scatter diagram that shows the data collected for the students in the group. Help the groups determine appropriate increments for the axes labels. Depending upon the variation in height, each line on the graph paper could represent 1 or 2 inches. On the shoe-size axis, each line will likely represent a half or a whole size.

Discuss the results as a class. Ask students if there seems to be a relationship between height and shoe size among the students in the class.

Using More than One Data Source

Problem Solver

SB p. 146

Lesson Objective

- use more than one source of data to solve word problems

Activity

Population Explosion

Purpose: reinforce the ideas in the lesson

Materials

- PCM 20: City Data, p. 73
- calculators
- graph paper

What to Do

Distribute a copy of PCM 20 and a calculator to each student. Tell students that this handout includes information about the population of several large cities in the United States and Europe. Explain that population is one way to describe the size of a city, but land area is also an important factor. If you compare the population with the land area, you can get an idea of how crowded the city is.

Say, *"Imagine that two cities have the same amount of area. One city has three million people, while the other city has one million people. Which city would be more crowded?"*

To illustrate square miles, draw a square on the board and label each side *5 miles.* Explain that the area within the boundaries of this square is 25 square miles. If possible, compare this with a local city or town that has an area of about 25 square miles.

Model how to calculate the population per square mile for a 25-square-mile city with a population of 110,000. Tell students to enter 110,000 on their calculators and then divide by 25. (4,400)

Have students solve problems 1–4 on PCM 20 and discuss their answers.

Give each student graph paper to use for problem 5 on PCM 20.

Simple and Compound Probability

SB p. 148

Lesson Objectives

- understand probability
- find simple probability
- find compound probability

Activity

Probability and Cards

Purpose: introduce the ideas in the lesson

Materials

- deck of playing cards

What to Do

Make sure students are familiar with the components of a deck of playing cards: 52 cards, 4 suits of 13 cards each, 2 red and 2 black suits, 4 cards for each number (2 through 10), and 4 each of jack, queen, king, ace.

Use the cards to show some examples of the probability of drawing a card at random.

- probability of selecting a 4 (1 in 13)
- probability of selecting a red card (1 in 2)
- probability of selecting the ace of spades (1 in 52)

Ask volunteers for other probability problems using the cards to present to the class.

Seeing Trends, Making Predictions

Problem Solver

SB p. 150

Lesson Objectives

- analyze data and probability to make predictions
- check a prediction

Activity

Testing Probability

Purpose: reinforce the ideas in the lesson

Materials

- PCM 21: Testing Probability, p. 74
- container for each group (bag, box, or bowl)

What to Do

Have students work in groups of 5. Have each student write his or her name on a piece of paper, fold the paper, and place it in the container. If a group has fewer than 5 people, ask them to use imaginary names to bring the total to 5.

Ask, *"What would be the probability of selecting a particular student's name at random?"* $\left(\frac{1}{5}\right)$ If the student's name is put back in the container, ask for the probability of selecting the same name two times in a row. $\left(\frac{1}{25}\right)$

Distribute a copy of PCM 21 to each group. Ask students to test these probabilities.

Groups should list members on the PCM under "Member." Members should then take turns closing their eyes and selecting a name from the container. Each name selected is recorded in the Trial 1 table on the PCM. Names are returned to the container after each selection. After making 25 selections, the group records the number of times each name was drawn. They record the successive events for Trial 1 by counting the number of times one member's name was selected two times in a row. Then have groups complete a second trial of 25 selections.

Discuss the results with the class. How close did the results come to the predictions of $\frac{1}{5}$ (selection per student) and $\frac{1}{25}$ (successive events)?

Mean, Median, and Mode

Application

SB p. 152

Lesson Objectives

- find the mean, median, and mode in sets of data
- understand when mean, median, and mode are accurate typical values

Activity

Typical Group Values

Purpose: reinforce the ideas in the lesson

What to Do

Have students work in groups of about seven or nine. Ask students to find the mean, median, and mode for some personal statistics. Groups can select from the following list or use other statistics:

- number of pets
- number of children
- number of times moved
- number of miles between home and school

What to Look For

When finding the mean, remind students to divide by the total number in the sample. Even if one member of the sample has a zero value, that member must still be included in the number used as the divisor.

Algebra and Geometry

Activity Overview

Student Book Lesson	Pages in SB	Pages in TRG	Activity Type	PCM Number
Writing Expressions	158	43	Communication	
The Number Line	160	43	Hands-On	
Powers and Roots	162	44	Hands-On	
Writing Equations	164	44	Communication	
Order of Operations	166	45	Reasoning	22
The Distributive Property	168	45	Mental Math	
Addition and Subtraction Equations	170	45	Hands-On	
Multiplication and Division Equations	172	46	Real-Life	23
Working with Formulas	174	46	Communication	
Substituting to Solve Equations	176	47	Real-Life	
Writing and Solving Inequalities	178	47	Making Connections	
Translating Words to Equations	180	48	Making Connections	
Points, Lines, and Angles	184	48	Cooperative Learning	
Protractors	186	48	Real-Life	
Types of Angles	188	49	Reasoning	
Circles	190	49	Hands-On	
Quadrilaterals	192	50	Reasoning	
Triangles	194	50	Hands-On	
Similar Geometric Figures	196	51	Hands-On	
Finding Patterns in Algebra and Geometry	198	51	Reasoning	
The Pythagorean Theorem	200	51	Hands-On	
Reading Maps	202	52	Hands-On	
Perimeter and Circumference	204	52	Real-Life	24
Area	206	53	Real-Life	24, 25
Volume	208	53	Hands-On	
Choosing Area, Perimeter, or Volume	210	53	Real-Life	
The Coordinate System	212	54	Hands-On	
Slope and Intercept	214	54	Hands-On	

Unit Overview

The purpose of this unit is to demonstrate ways to use algebra and geometry to solve problems. Students will gain an understanding of equations and their role in problem solving. Students will also study geometric properties and formulas.

When Do I Use Algebra and Geometry? page 157

Encourage students to talk about everyday calculations. Then have students name the shapes of common household items, such as tables or windows. Ask why you would need the measurements of such objects. Have students check the algebra and geometry experiences at the top of the page they have had. Then have them read questions 1–4 and describe how they would solve these problems.

Talk About It page 157

Have students fold a piece of paper into eight equal pieces and cut out the rectangles. Tell students to rearrange the pieces. Ask if the pieces can be placed next to one another without leaving space. Now have students cut out several shapes that don't have right angles and rearrange these figures in a similar manner. Discuss how angles affect the way shapes fit together. Note that the same size figures with right angles will fit together easily. It's harder to construct figures without right angles that fit together.

Working Together page 217

Give students maps that show a rectangular area. Review how to use a legend or key to determine actual miles. After students measure the perimeter, ask them what formula they will use to calculate the number of square miles covered. Then have them use the formula for the area of a rectangle to calculate the area in square miles.

Writing Expressions

SB p. 158

Lesson Objectives

- write expressions that use addition, subtraction, multiplication, and division to represent word problems
- write expressions that use letters for unknown amounts
- understand inverse operations

Activity

Words and Expressions

Purpose: reinforce the ideas in the lesson

Materials

- index cards

What to Do

Write these expressions on the board: $25 + 10$; $25 - 10$; $25(10)$; $25 \div 10$.

For each expression, have students write a problem that reflects the correct use of the operation. Give this example: *"If Joan took a twenty-five-minute bus ride and then walked ten minutes to reach her job, how long did it take her to get there?"* ($25 + 10$) Collect and number the problems.

Give each student four index cards. Have students copy each of the expressions onto a separate card. Tell students that you are going to read the problems one at a time. Students are to listen carefully and decide which operation they would use to solve each problem. They should then select the expression that reflects that operation and write the problem number on the appropriate index card. (You can vary the length of the activity by using fewer or more problems in this step.)

Compare and discuss students' choices. Use the answers to the expressions (35, 15, 250, 2.5) to help students decide if their choice makes sense for the given problem.

The Number Line

Tools

SB p. 160

Lesson Objective

- use number lines to add and subtract signed numbers

Activity

Aim for Zero

Purpose: reinforce the ideas in the lesson

Materials

- index cards

What to Do

Have students work in pairs. Distribute 40 index cards to each pair. Have them make a card for each signed number –10 through +10. Have them make 10 cards for the + symbol and 10 cards for the – symbol. Have them shuffle the number cards and the symbol cards and place each pile facedown.

Everyone starts with a score of 0. Partners take turns picking up a symbol card and a number card to create an expression with their current score and record the value, which becomes their new score. For example, if in three turns a student drew the cards – (–5), + (+2) and – (+4), the score at the end of three rounds would be 3. [$0 - (-5) = 5$; $5 + (+2) = 7$; $7 - (+4) = 3$]

When all cards have been used, the player with the score closer to 0 wins.

Powers and Roots

SB p. 162

Lesson Objectives

- understand powers and roots
- solve powers
- create a table of common perfect squares
- find square roots of perfect squares
- find ranges for square roots
- use a calculator to find square roots

Activity

Penny Power

Purpose: introduce the ideas in the lesson

Materials

- pennies or other counters

What to Do

To demonstrate the concept of powers, have students work in groups. Give each group 27 pennies.

1. Tell students to place 3 pennies in a row. Explain that this group of pennies can represent the power 3^1.
2. Have students make 3 rows of 3 pennies. Tell them this represents 3×3, or 3^2. Ask students to count or multiply to find the value of 3^2. (9)
3. Tell students to stack the pennies to make 9 stacks of 3 pennies. Have them put the 9 stacks in 3 rows of 3. Show how this represents 3 columns $\times$ 3 rows $\times$ 3 in each stack, or 3^3. Ask students to determine the value of 3^3. (27)

Writing Equations

SB p. 164

Lesson Objectives

- write an algebraic equation for a verbal expression and vice versa
- match equations and verbal expressions
- select an equation to represent a situation described in words

Activity

Numbers and Words

Purpose: introduce the ideas in the lesson

What to Do

Help students think about the relationships between equations and words. On the board, write $5 + 4 = 9$. Describe different ways to express this equation verbally. (Five increased by four is nine. The sum of five and four is nine. Four added to five is nine.)

On the board, write the names of the four basic operations. Ask students to think of different words and phrases that are used to express the operations (for subtraction: difference, less than, take away; for multiplication: multiplied by, times; for division: divided by, separated into). List responses with the appropriate operation.

Then write an equation for each operation. Some sample answers are $6 + 3 = 9$; $18 - 5 = 13$; $4 \times 8 = 32$; $25 \div 5 = 5$. Ask students to express these equations verbally in as many ways as possible.

Order of Operations

SB p. 166

Lesson Objectives

- understand the order of operations
- evaluate expressions using the order of operations
- write an expression for a given situation

Common Difficulties

Students may have trouble remembering the order of operations. Suggest that they copy the example on student book page 166 onto a card they can refer to.

Activity

Order the Operations

Purpose: reinforce the ideas in the lesson

Materials

- PCM 22: Order the Operations, p. 75

What to Do

Have students use a step-by-step approach to identify each calculation needed to evaluate a multiple-operation expression.

Distribute a copy of PCM 22 to each student. Model the first problem:

$3(6 + 4)^2$

a. $6 + 4 = 10$

b. $10^2 = 100$

c. $3(100) = 300$

Have students complete the handout. Discuss students' solutions after they finish.

What to Look For

Remind students that in the order of operations, division is at the same level as multiplication, and subtraction is at the same level as addition.

The Distributive Property

SB p. 168

Lesson Objectives

- understand the distributive property
- use the distributive property to write expressions for problems
- use a formula to calculate the area of a rectangle

Activity

Mental Math

Purpose: extend the ideas in the lesson

What to Do

Tell students that the distributive property can be used to simplify mental math calculations. Write the following problem on the board: 88×6. Show students how to use the distributive property to rewrite this expression: $(80 + 8)6$ or $(80 \times 6) + (8 \times 6)$. The second expression includes numbers that are easy to work with mentally. $(480 + 48 = 528)$

Continue with a money problem: $\$3.98 \times 5$; $[(\$4.00 \times 5) - (\$0.02 \times 5) = \$19.90]$.

Write the following problems on the board for students to solve mentally.

1. What is the cost of 3 picture frames at $7.99 apiece? $[(\$8.00 \times 3) - (\$.01 \times 3) = \$23.97]$
2. How many seats are available in a room with 40 rows of 12 seats? $[(40 \times 10) + (40 \times 2) = 480]$
3. What is the cost of 2 pounds of roast beef at $4.49 per pound? $[(\$4.50 \times 2) - (\$.01 \times 2) = \$8.98]$
4. What is the total number of juice cans in 8 cases of 24 cans? $[(20 \times 8) + (4 \times 8) = 192]$

Addition and Subtraction Equations

SB p. 170

Lesson Objectives

- use inverse operations to solve addition and subtraction equations
- use addition and subtraction equations to solve word problems

Activity

The Balancing Act

Purpose: introduce the ideas in the lesson

Materials

- objects to be used as counters
- masking tape

What to Do

Use manipulatives to introduce the concept of balancing both sides of an equation. Have students work in pairs, and give each pair 20 counters and some tape. Follow these instructions:

1. Ask students to use the tape to make an equal sign on their desks. Have them place 5 counters on each side of the equal sign and write an equation to represent this situation. ($5 = 5$)

2. Tell students to remove 2 counters from one side of the = and write an expression to represent this action and result. ($5 - 2 = 5$) Ask, *"Are both sides equal?"* (no) *"What can you do to make both sides equal?"* (Take 2 counters from the right side of =.) Tell students to write an equation to represent this new situation. ($5 - 2 = 5 - 2$)

3. Provide other combinations of counters and have students add and subtract to maintain a balance.

Multiplication and Division Equations

SB p. 172

Lesson Objectives

- use inverse operations to solve multiplication and division equations
- solve one- and two-step multiplication and division equations
- use multiplication and division equations to solve word problems

Activity

Order Form

Purpose: reinforce the ideas in the lesson

Materials

- PCM 23: Order Form, p. 76

What to Do

Distribute a copy of PCM 23 to each student. Have students use the price list to write equations and solve the word problems. Discuss their equations and solutions.

What to Look For

You may need to remind students that like variables can be added and subtracted using the coefficients (the numbers by which the variables are multiplied), for example, $3x + 2x = 5x$.

Working with Formulas

Application

SB p. 174

Lesson Objectives

- understand equivalent formulas
- write equivalent formulas to solve problems

Activity

What's the Formula?

Purpose: reinforce the ideas in the lesson

Materials

- newspaper help-wanted ads

What to Do

Give students this example of a commonly used formula: hours worked (h) $\times$ rate (r) = total pay (T) or $hr = T$.

Ask students to write the equivalent equations to solve for the other unknowns in this formula. ($r = \frac{T}{h}$ and $h = \frac{T}{r}$)

Have students work in pairs to write a problem using this formula. Give each pair a newspaper section to look through for examples of hourly or weekly pay rates. They can use the rates with values they make up to create a problem. Pairs can exchange problems and use the formula to find the answers.

Substituting to Solve Equations

Problem Solver

SB p. 176

Lesson Objectives

- substitute values to solve equations
- solve an equation for one value to substitute in another equation
- substitute an expression for a variable to solve an equation
- use substitution to solve word problems

Common Difficulties

Make sure students understand which variable is the unknown being solved for. Encourage students to ask questions if this concept is unclear.

Activity

Overtime Pay

Purpose: extend the ideas in the lesson

What to Do

Show students how substitution in an equation can be used to figure total pay with overtime. Explain that businesses are required to pay hourly workers an overtime rate for hours worked over 40 hours a week. The law sets this rate at 1.5 times the regular rate (time and a half).

1. On the board, list the following: r = rate of pay, h = hours worked in 1 week, p = total weekly pay. Ask students to write an equation that could be used to find the total weekly pay for a 40-hour worker. ($40r = p$)

2. Have students use r to write an expression that shows the pay rate for the hours worked over 40 hours a week. ($1.5r$) Ask students to use h to write an expression that shows the number of hours worked over 40 in a week. ($h - 40$)

3. Help students put these expressions together to write an equation for figuring total pay with overtime. [$40r + (h - 40)(1.5r) = p$] Have students substitute values in the new equation to solve the following overtime problems. Both problems assume a 40-hour workweek and overtime pay of 1.5 times the regular rate.

   - Connie worked 48 hours in 1 week and earned \$624. What is Connie's regular rate of pay? (\$12.00 per hour)
   - Andrew worked 45 hours in 1 week. His regular pay rate is $\frac{\$9.25}{\text{hour}}$. That same week, Donna earned \$40 more than Andrew. What was Donna's pay that week? (\$479.40)

What to Look For

You may need to discuss why 1.5 can be used to determine overtime pay. Explain that $1\frac{1}{2}$ equals 1.5, so finding $1\frac{1}{2}$ times the regular rate is the same as multiplying the regular rate by 1.5.

Writing and Solving Inequalities

SB p. 178

Lesson Objectives

- write and solve inequalities for given situations
- graph inequalities on a number line
- use inequalities to solve word problems

Activity

Inequalities and Number Lines

Purpose: introduce the ideas in the lesson

Materials

- poster board or large piece of paper
- sales circulars from department stores

What to Do

Draw a number line on a piece of poster board. Label the line with points for –10 through 10. Circle the number 4 on the line and ask students to name some numbers that are less than 4. Explain that 4 is not a member of the set of numbers that are less than 4. Invite a volunteer to darken the number line to represent the set of all numbers that are less than 4. The circled 4 remains unshaded.

On a separate number line, color in the circle on the 4. Now ask students to name some numbers that are greater than or equal to 4. Emphasize that 4 is a member of the set of numbers because 4 is equal to 4.

Invite a volunteer to darken the number line to represent the set of all numbers that are greater than or equal to 4.

Now have students apply this concept to a real-world setting. Reinforce the concepts of inequalities and upper or lower limits with the following activity.

Have students work in groups and give each group one or two sales flyers. Pose problem situations like this one: *"I spent less than eighty-nine dollars on two small appliances. What are some possible pairs of appliances whose costs fit this description?"* Have students find a pair of items that fits each situation.

Translating Words to Equations

Problem Solver

SB p. 180

Lesson Objectives

- organize information from a problem in a chart
- create charts to solve problems

Activity

Unequal Investments

Purpose: reinforce the ideas in the lesson

What to Do

To practice the concepts in this lesson, present the following problem.

"Four friends, Arthur, Barbara, Carmen, and Douglas, decide to form an investment group. They each put in an amount of money. The group decides where to invest the total amount. Any earnings from the investment are divided in proportion to each person's original investment. Barbara invests three times as much as Arthur, Carmen invests one and a half times as much as Arthur, and Douglas invests half as much as Arthur."

Have students use a chart similar to those in the lesson to find the proportion of each person's investment. [Arthur (A) = x; Barbara (B) = $3x$; Carmen (C) = $\frac{3x}{2}$; Douglas (D) = $\frac{x}{2}$]

Give students different earning figures, and have them find each investor's portion. Some examples: $900 and $1,500.

($900: A = $150, B = $450, C = $225, D = $75)

($1,500: A = $250, B = $750, C = $375, D = $125)

Points, Lines, and Angles

SB p. 184

Lesson Objectives

- understand the properties of points, lines, and angles
- identify illustrations that match particular properties

Activity

Geometric Scavenger Hunt

Purpose: reinforce the ideas in the lesson

What to Do

Have students work in small groups. Write the following headings on the board: *Parallel Lines, Perpendicular Lines, Right Angles, Acute Angles,* and *Obtuse Angles*. Explain that groups will be given 10 minutes to list real-life examples in each category.

At the end of 10 minutes, score the lists. Each valid item is worth 1 point. Each category that has at least 1 valid item is worth 2 points. For example, a group that had valid items for only right angles and parallel lines would score 4 points plus 1 point for each valid item listed.

Expansion/Reinforcement: Play a second round of the game, having students select examples of lines and angles from magazines, newspapers, or flyers.

Protractors

Tools

SB p. 186

Lesson Objectives

- use a protractor to measure angles
- calculate measures of angles

Activity

Clock Angles

Purpose: reinforce the ideas in the lesson

What to Do

Remind students that there are 360° in a circle. Ask students to write the measure of the angles formed by the hands on a clock at each hour of the day:

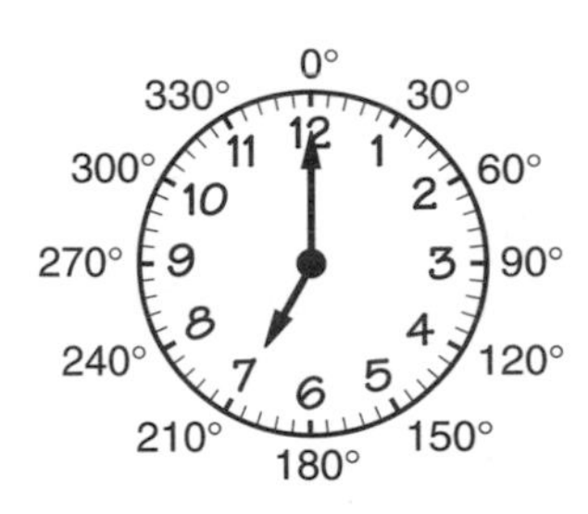

Types of Angles

SB p. 188

Lesson Objectives

- recognize different types of angles and understand their relationships with one another
- calculate the measures of complementary, supplementary, and vertical angles
- apply geometric principles to planning city streets

Activity

Transversal

Purpose: extend the ideas in the lesson

Materials

- graph paper

What to Do

Distribute a piece of graph paper to each student. Tell students to draw two parallel, vertical lines. Then have students draw a straight line that intersects the parallel lines and label the angles with consecutive numbers, as in the drawing below.

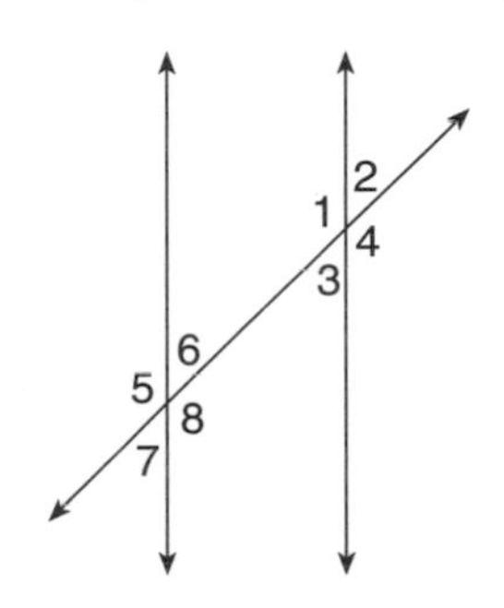

Tell students that the line that intersects two parallel lines is called a *transversal.* Point out that corresponding angles of the two intersections are equal: $\angle 1$ and $\angle 5$, $\angle 2$ and $\angle 6$, $\angle 3$ and $\angle 7$, and $\angle 4$ and $\angle 8$. Ask, *"Which pairs of angles are vertical and therefore equal?"* ($\angle 1$ and $\angle 4$, $\angle 2$ and $\angle 3$, $\angle 6$ and $\angle 7$, $\angle 5$ and $\angle 8$)

Explain that since $\angle 1$ and $\angle 4$ are equal and $\angle 4$ and $\angle 8$ are equal, $\angle 1$ and $\angle 8$ are equal. Have students use what they know about supplementary angles to find other pairs of equal angles. ($\angle 3$ and $\angle 6$, $\angle 2$ and $\angle 7$, $\angle 4$ and $\angle 5$)

Circles

SB p. 190

Lesson Objectives

- understand and use the characteristics of a circle
- use the formula $C = \pi d$ to find circumference of a circle
- practice partitioning circles

Activity

Measuring Circumference

Purpose: reinforce the ideas in the lesson

Materials

- objects with circular bases, such as cans, cups, or bowls
- string, rulers, and scissors

What to Do

Tell students that they will measure the circumference of a circle to test the circumference formula. Have them work in pairs. Give each pair string, a ruler, scissors, and an object with a circular base.

Ask pairs to measure the diameter of the circle and then use the formula to find the circumference of the circle. Next have them place the string around the edge of the circle and mark it or cut it to a length that equals the circumference. Tell students to measure the length of the string. Ask, *"How does this measurement compare with the circumference calculated with the formula?"* Discuss students' results.

Quadrilaterals

SB p. 192

Lesson Objectives

- recognize different kinds of quadrilaterals
- understand and use the properties of quadrilaterals

Common Difficulties

Make sure students understand that some figures can be labeled as more than one kind of quadrilateral. A square can also be called a rectangle, a parallelogram, and a rhombus.

Activity

Plane Figures and Angles

Purpose: extend the ideas in the lesson

What to Do

Using the properties of a square, have students determine the sum of the measures of its angles. (360°) Explain that all quadrilaterals have angles whose sum equals 360°.

Introduce the formula for finding the sum of the angles in other polygons: Sum $= 180°(n - 2)$, where n is the number of sides in the polygon.

Have students find the sum of the angles in figures with 5, 6, 8, and 10 sides. (540°, 720°, 1,080°, and 1,440°)

Triangles

SB p. 194

Lesson Objectives

- identify the four kinds of triangles
- understand and use the properties of different kinds of triangles

Activity

Sides of Triangles

Purpose: extend the ideas in the lesson

Materials

- cotton swabs or toothpicks

What to Do

Introduce the relationships between the sides of a triangle. Tell students that in any triangle, the length of any side must be less than the sum of the other two sides. The length of any side must also be greater than the difference between the other two sides.

Distribute 4 cotton swabs or toothpicks to each student. Have students use the objects to explore these concepts. Use 2 toothpicks to form two sides of a triangle. Place them at a right angle. Use two other toothpicks to form a third side. Point out that the length of this third side equals the sum of the other two sides. Try to form a triangle by increasing the angle of the first two sides. Those two sides become a straight line. The figure cannot be a triangle.

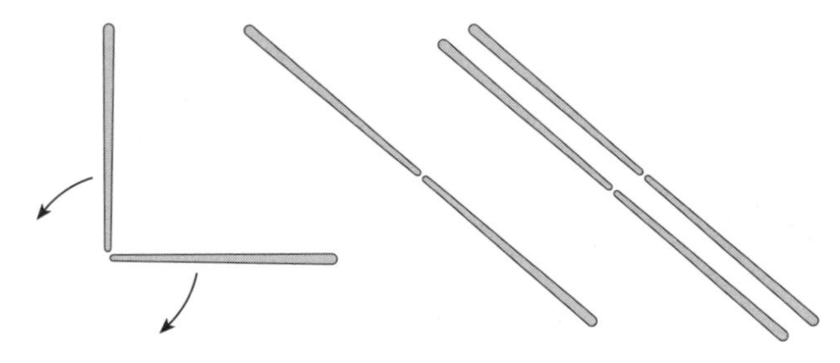

Students can also use the 4 toothpicks to explore why the third side of a triangle must be greater than the difference between the other two sides. Have students use three toothpicks to form a right angle, with two toothpicks forming the first side and one toothpick forming the second side. If the length of the third side were equal to the difference in length of the other sides (1 toothpick), then the sides of the triangle would collapse and fall on top of each other. This cannot be a triangle.

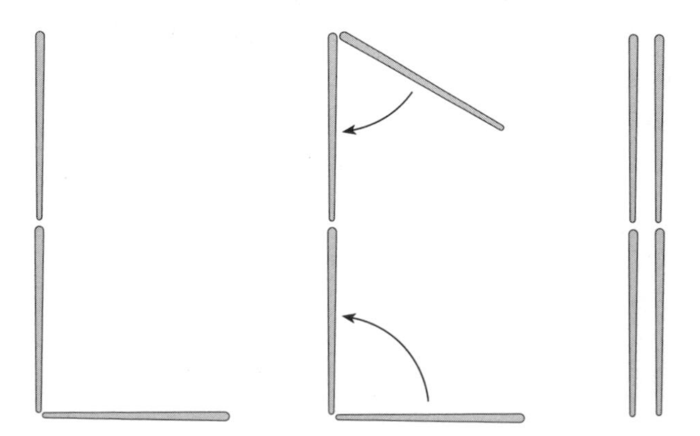

Similar Geometric Figures

SB p. 196

Lesson Objectives

- understand the properties of similar figures
- use proportion to find missing sides of similar figures
- use proportion to find the height of tall objects

Activity

Drawing Similar Figures

Purpose: introduce the ideas in the lesson

Materials

- graph paper, rulers, and protractors

What to Do

Students can construct similar right triangles and rectangles and then explore the properties of similar figures. Distribute graph paper, a ruler, and a protractor to each student.

1. Tell students to draw two sides of a right triangle with a vertical segment measuring 4 units and a horizontal segment measuring 3 units. Students then draw a line to connect the two segments.
2. Tell students to draw another right triangle with the horizontal and vertical sides twice the lengths of the first triangle's sides. Have them measure the hypotenuse in both figures. Ask, *"What is the ratio of the hypotenuses?"* (The ratio of the longer hypotenuse to the shorter one is 2:1.)
3. If protractors are available, have students measure and compare corresponding angles in the similar figures to determine that these angles are equal.
4. Tell students to draw a rectangle and label its width and length. Then tell students to draw a similar rectangle that is larger than the original and another similar rectangle that is smaller. They should label the widths and lengths of both new rectangles. After they finish, make sure students have understood that the width and length of each new rectangle should increase or decrease at the same rate.

Finding Patterns in Algebra and Geometry

Problem Solver

SB p. 198

Lesson Objectives

- find patterns in number and letter series
- find patterns in the measures of similar figures
- use tables and charts to find patterns

Activity

Patterns and Expressions

Purpose: extend the ideas in the lesson

Materials

- SB pp. 198–199

What to Do

Show students how to write expressions to describe patterns. For example, the pattern in problem 1 on student book page 198 can be expressed as $x + 3$. An expression for problem 2 is $x - 9$. Have students write expressions for problems 1–4 and 6.

Then have students look at Part C on student book page 199. Point out that the sides of the rectangles in the table increase by 1. Ask students to write an expression that shows how the perimeter of these rectangles increases as each side increases by 1. $(p + 4)$

Ask volunteers to share the expressions they wrote.

The Pythagorean Theorem

SB p. 200

Lesson Objectives

- become familiar with the formula for the Pythagorean theorem
- use the Pythagorean theorem to find missing sides of right triangles

- use the Pythagorean theorem to solve word problems

Activity

Proving the Pythagorean Theorem

Purpose: extend the ideas in the lesson

Materials

- sheets of $8\frac{1}{2}$-by-11-inch paper
- calculators and rulers

What to Do

Give each student a sheet of $8\frac{1}{2}$-by-11-inch paper. Make sure each student has a calculator and a ruler to use. Ask them to fold the paper in half, matching the $8\frac{1}{2}$-inch edges, and then draw a diagonal for this rectangle.

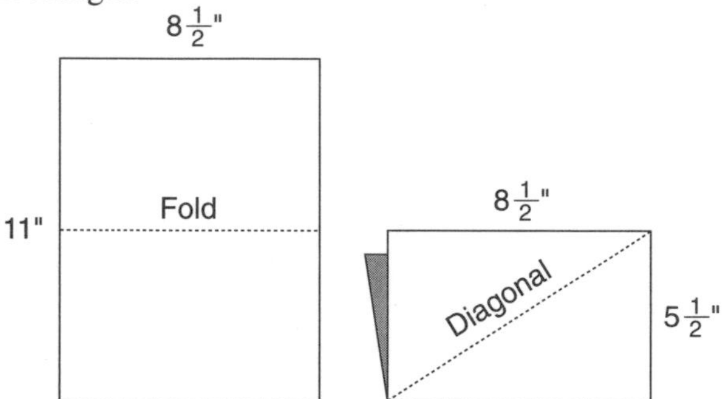

Tell students that the sides of this rectangle measure $8\frac{1}{2}$ inches and $5\frac{1}{2}$ inches. Have students use the Pythagorean theorem and a calculator to find the length of the hypotenuse ($\approx$ 10.12 inches). Now have students measure the diagonal. They should discover that the hypotenuse measures just slightly more than 10 inches.

This activity can be done with rectangles of different sizes.

Reading Maps

Application

SB p. 202

Lesson Objectives

- understand that scales on maps represent proportions
- use proportion to solve distance problems based on maps

Activity

Reading Local Maps

Purpose: reinforce the ideas in the lesson

Materials

- maps of local cities or state road maps
- rulers

What to Do

Have students work in pairs and give each pair a map and a ruler. Help students locate the key or legend on the map.

Have pairs select two or three points on their map. They should measure the straight-line distances between the points and use the scale to calculate actual mileage. Then, using the scale given in the key, have them estimate the distance by existing roadways. Students' choice of roadways may vary depending on directness of route or ease of use (speed limits, accessibility, lack of stoplights, and so on).

Perimeter and Circumference

SB p. 204

Lesson Objectives

- use formulas to find the perimeter or circumference of different plane figures
- use perimeter and circumference to solve problems

Activity

Landscape Design

Purpose: reinforce the ideas in the lesson

Materials

- PCM 24: Landscape Design, p. 77
- calculators

What to Do

Distribute a copy of PCM 24 and a calculator to each student. Have students use what they have learned about perimeter and circumference to solve the problems. Discuss their answers when they finish. You may want to ask students to save their copies of PCM 24 to use with the next activity.

Area

SB p. 206

Lesson Objectives

- use formulas to find the area of different plane figures
- use area to solve problems

Common Difficulties

Students may have difficulty understanding why area is measured in square units. If necessary, draw a 4-inch square divided into 1-inch squares to illustrate this concept.

Activity

Design and Area

Purpose: reinforce the ideas in the lesson

Materials

- PCM 24: Landscape Design, p. 77
- PCM 25: Design and Area, p. 78

What to Do

Ask students to take out their copies of PCM 24 to use with this activity. Distribute a copy of PCM 25 to each student. Tell students to use the drawing on PCM 24 to solve the problems on PCM 25. Discuss students' answers when they finish.

Volume

SB p. 208

Lesson Objectives

- calculate volume for rectangular solids, cubes, and cylinders
- use volume to solve problems

Activity

Measuring Volume

Purpose: reinforce the ideas in the lesson

Materials

- containers and objects that are rectangular solids, cubes, and cylinders (boxes, blocks, cans, tubes, etc.)
- rulers

What to Do

Students can explore volume by calculating volumes of different objects and containers. Have students work in small groups. Give each group two or three items. Depending upon the kinds of objects available, ask students to predict which objects will have a larger or smaller volume. They can then test their predictions. Have students measure the dimensions and use the formulas to calculate volume. Students can refer to the volume formulas on student book page 208.

Choosing Area, Perimeter, or Volume

Problem Solver

SB p. 210

Lesson Objectives

- identify the appropriate measure (area, perimeter, or volume) for a given situation
- identify the appropriate units of measure for area, perimeter, and volume problems
- solve area, perimeter, and volume problems
- estimate with π

Activity

What Measurement?

Purpose: reinforce the ideas in the lesson

What to Do

Ask each student to write a description of a situation in which area, perimeter, or volume could be measured. Give an example, such as the amount of wall space to be covered with wallpaper (area). Tell students to describe the situation without mentioning the type of measurement needed.

Collect students' descriptions and select some to read to the class. Ask volunteers to name the kind of measurement needed (area, perimeter, or volume) for each situation.

The Coordinate System

SB p. 212

Lesson Objectives

- understand the function of a coordinate system
- identify points on a coordinate system
- find the distance between points on a coordinate system

Activity

Figures in the Coordinate System

Purpose: reinforce the ideas in the lesson

Materials

- graph paper

What to Do

This drawing activity will give students practice working with a coordinate system and identifying ordered pairs.

Distribute two sheets of graph paper to each student. Tell students to construct two coordinate systems by drawing *x*- and *y*-axes and labeling them from –12 to +12. Then ask students to draw a different polygon in each quadrant of one system. Students should label all vertices on the figures with the appropriate ordered pairs.

Then have students work in pairs. Ask partners to take turns dictating the ordered pairs in each of the figures they drew. The other partner plots the points on the blank coordinate system and reproduces the figures.

Slope and Intercept

SB p. 214

Lesson Objectives

- calculate slope of a line on a coordinate system
- find the *x*- and *y*-intercepts of a line on a coordinate system

Activity

Slopes and Roofs

Purpose: extend the ideas in the lesson

Materials

- graph paper

What to Do

Explain that roof construction applies the concept of slope. The slope, or incline, of a roof is calculated using the ratio of vertical rise to horizontal run. It can be expressed as a distance in 12 (inches), for example, 4 inches vertical rise in 12 inches of horizontal run.

Distribute graph paper to students. Tell students to draw a grid, labeling the *x*-axis from 0 to 24 and the *y*-axis from 0 to 12. Have students draw lines to represent roofs with 4 in 12 slope, 5 in 12 slope, and 6 in 12 slope. Suggest that students find 2 points for each line (x in 12 in. and $2x$ in 24 in.) and then connect the points.

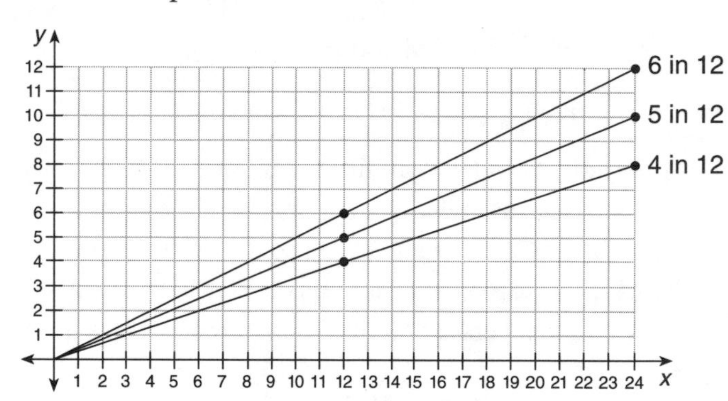

PCM 1

Household Budgets

Budget #1

	Monthly	Yearly
Income:		
Take-home pay	$1,825.00	
Expenses:		
Rent	$475.00	
Utilities	160.00	
Transportation	70.00	
Telephone	40.00	
Food	520.00	
Insurance	55.00	
Miscellaneous	190.00	
Total Expenses	$1,510.00	

Budget #2

	Monthly	Yearly
Income:		
Take-home pay		
Expenses:		
Rent		
Utilities		
Transportation		
Telephone		
Food		
Clothing		
Medical Care		
Entertainment		
Savings		
Insurance		
Miscellaneous		
Total Expenses		

PCM 2

Problem Cards

Problem 1

Your doctor advises you to limit your daily intake of fat to less than 65 grams. Today you eat three meals. They contain 12 grams, 21 grams, and 26 grams of fat. Do you stay within the daily limit?

- **a.** What is the question?
- **b.** What information is needed?
- **c.** What strategy should you use?
- **d.** Estimate an answer.
- **e.** What is the solution?

Problem 1 Answers

- **a.** Do you stay under the limit of 65 grams of fat per day?
- **b.** fat content of 3 meals (12 grams, 21 grams, 26 grams) and daily total allowed (65 grams)
- **c.** add
- **d.** Round to estimate: $10 + 20 + 30 = 60$
- **e.** $12 + 21 + 26 = 59$ Yes, you ate less than 65 grams of fat.

Problem 2

To avoid paying extra charges on her leased vehicle, Mariel tries to keep the yearly mileage to 15,000. In 10 months, she put on 12,638 miles. What mileage limit will Mariel set for the next 2 months?

- **a.** What is the question?
- **b.** What information is needed?
- **c.** What strategy should you use?
- **d.** Estimate an answer.
- **e.** What is the solution?

Problem 2 Answers

- **a.** What mileage limit will Mariel set for the next 2 months?
- **b.** total miles driven in 10 months (12,638) and total yearly allowance (15,000)
- **c.** subtract
- **d.** Estimate: $15{,}000 - 12{,}600 = 2{,}400$
- **e.** $15{,}000 - 12{,}638 = 2{,}362$

Problem 3

A trucker drives a daily route from New York City to the Boston area and back. This round trip is 418 miles. How many miles does the trucker drive during an average 5-day workweek?

- **a.** What is the question?
- **b.** What information is needed?
- **c.** What strategy should you use?
- **d.** Estimate an answer.
- **e.** What is the solution?

Problem 3 Answers

- **a.** How many miles does the trucker drive during an average workweek?
- **b.** daily total of miles (418) and number of days in the workweek (5)
- **c.** multiply
- **d.** Estimate: $400 \times 5 = 2{,}000$
- **e.** $418 \times 5 = 2{,}090$

Problem 4

A patio design is 192 inches long. The 12-inch-wide blocks will be placed side by side along this edge. How many blocks will the patio have along this edge?

- **a.** What is the question?
- **b.** What information is needed?
- **c.** What strategy should you use?
- **d.** Estimate an answer.
- **e.** What is the solution?

Problem 4 Answers

- **a.** How many blocks will be along the patio's edge?
- **b.** length of patio (192 inches) and width of block (12 inches)
- **c.** divide
- **d.** Estimate: $190 \div 10 = 19$
- **e.** $192 \div 12 = 16$

PCM 3

Number Grid

799	108	525	225	452	68
372	201	533	95	102	268
517	694	672	185	320	489
178	389	581	111	79	285
308	220	168	196	288	704
643	267	609	265	203	400
280	727	194	497	85	35
175	412	274	269	147	180
294	430	113	130	80	398
695	402	510	91	87	26

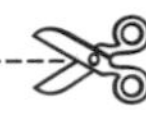

Decimal Models

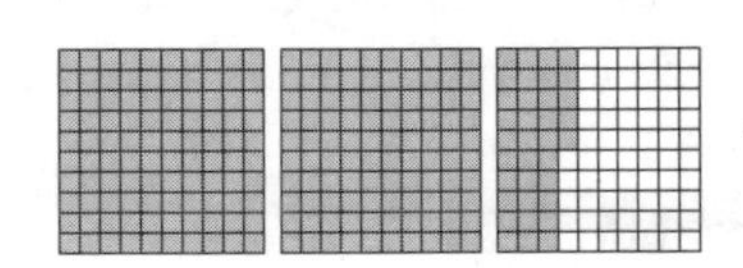

1. ______

4. ______

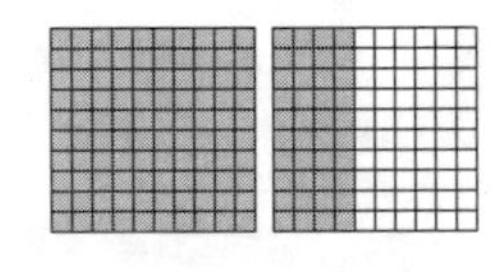

7. ______

2. ______

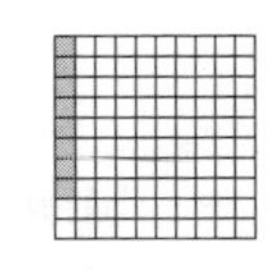

5. ______

8. ______

3. ______

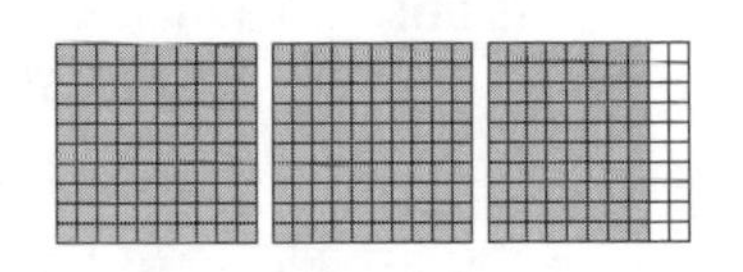

6. ______

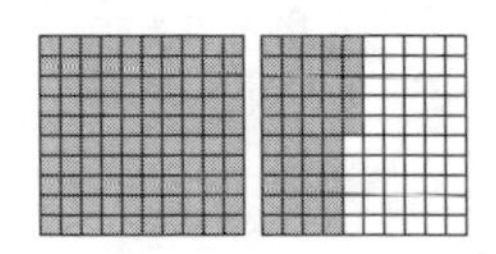

9. ______

PCM 5

Situation Cards

Problem 1
You are a cashier at a convenience store. A customer has made a purchase, and the display on the cash register tells you to give back $6.37 in change. What would you give the customer for change using the fewest bills and coins?

Answer: 1 five-dollar bill, 1 one-dollar bill, 1 quarter, 1 dime, and 2 pennies

Problem 2
You are writing a check to the telephone company for $32.76. How would you write this amount in words on the check?

Answer: Thirty-two and 76/100

Problem 3
You are in a job interview. The manager tells you that the job pays nine dollars and twenty-five cents per hour. Write a note to yourself so you remember this information.

Answer: pay = $9.25 per hour

Problem 4
A legal document states that you will make twelve equal payments of ninety-five dollars and forty-eight cents, for a total of one thousand one hundred forty-five dollars and seventy-six cents. Write this information in shorthand form with numbers.

Answer: 12 equal payments of $95.48 for a total of $1,145.76

Problem 5
You are approaching a tollbooth with a sign that says "Exact change. No pennies please." The amount of the toll is 50¢. Name 3 different combinations of coins you could use to pay the toll.

Answer: 1 half dollar; 2 quarters; 1 quarter, 2 dimes, 1 nickel; 1 quarter, 1 dime, 3 nickels; 1 quarter, 5 nickels; 5 dimes; 4 dimes, 2 nickels; 3 dimes, 4 nickels; 2 dimes, 6 nickels; 1 dime, 8 nickels; 10 nickels

Problem 6
You are in a department store and the cashier says, "That will be forty-five dollars and ninety-two cents." Write the numbers you would see on the cash register display.

Answer: $45.92

Problem 7
You are talking on the telephone to an electrician to get a price for repairs in your house. He says the job estimate is one hundred twenty-five dollars, of which twenty-eight dollars and ninety cents is for materials. Write a message with this information.

Answer: estimate = $125.00; $28.90 is for materials

Problem 8
Your boss asks you to prepare a bill for repairs made to a computer. She would like you to write the amounts in both words and numbers. The charge for labor is $75.00 and the charge for parts is $42.65, for a total of $117.65. Prepare this bill.

Answer: Labor $75.00 seventy-five dollars
Parts $42.65 forty-two dollars and sixty-five cents
Total $117.65 one hundred seventeen dollars and sixty-five cents

Paycheck Deductions Work Sheets

Use the amounts given in the first work sheet to calculate the net pay. Then create two more problems using other amounts for gross pay and deductions. Exchange work sheets with a partner and solve for net pay.

		Taxes		Other Deductions	
Gross Pay:	$320	Federal:	$25.59	Health Insurance:	$38.50
Less Taxes:		State:	12.82	Life Insurance:	
Less Other Deductions:		FICA:	19.18	Savings Plan:	10.75
Net Pay:		Total:		Union Dues:	
				Other:	
				Total:	

		Taxes		Other Deductions	
Gross Pay:		Federal:		Health Insurance:	
Less Taxes:		State:		Life Insurance:	
Less Other Deductions:		FICA:		Savings Plan:	
Net Pay:		Total:		Union Dues:	
				Other:	
				Total:	

		Taxes		Other Deductions	
Gross Pay:		Federal:		Health Insurance:	
Less Taxes:		State:		Life Insurance:	
Less Other Deductions:		FICA:		Savings Plan:	
Net Pay:		Total:		Union Dues:	
				Other:	
				Total:	

PCM 7

What Rates?

1. The rate of pay for a job is $12.50 per hour. What would be the total pay for

   a. 40 hours? ___________

   b. 24 hours? ___________

   c. 30 hours? ___________

2. A rental outlet charges $36.50 per day to rent a tile cutter. The tool can be rented for full or half days. What would be the rental charge for

   a. 2 days? ___________

   b. 5 days? ___________

   c. 1.5 days? ___________

3. The town of Midvale has an annual real estate tax of $12.57 per $1,000 of property value. What would be the annual tax on property valued at

   a. $78,000? ___________

   b. $124,000? ___________

   c. $95,000 ___________

   (*Hint:* Remove the zeros in the amounts to find how many thousands there are.)

4. The sticker on a new car reports the gas mileage as 21.2 miles per gallon. How far could you drive on

   a. 16 gallons of gas? _____

   b. 12 gallons of gas? _____

   c. 8.5 gallons of gas? _____

5. A study reports that teens spend an average of 1.6 hours per school night on homework. What would be the total hours for

   a. 4 nights? ___________

   b. 15 nights? ___________

   c. 9 nights? ___________

6. A newspaper article states that the town of Springfield spends an average of $21.50 per student annually on textbooks. What would be the total cost for

   a. 1,641 students? _______

   b. 2,897 students? _______

   c. 2,076 students? _______

7. On one day a British bank advertises an exchange rate of 1 British pound for 1.59 U.S. dollars. How many dollars would be exchanged for

   a. 50 pounds? _________

   b. 120 pounds? _________

   c. 245 pounds? _________

8. The current rate for heating oil is $.97 per gallon. What will be the cost for a delivery of

   a. 184 gallons? _________

   b. 208 gallons? _________

   c. 79 gallons? _________

PCM 8

Part and Whole Models

1.

$\frac{\text{part}}{\text{whole}}$ ________ decimal ________

2. 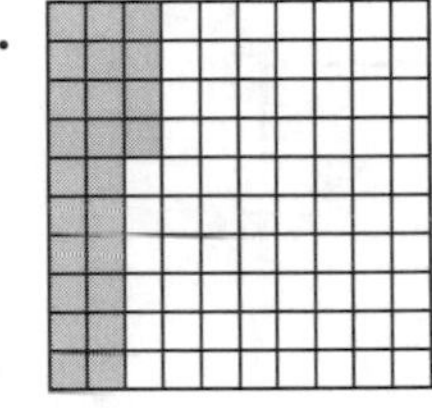

$\frac{\text{part}}{\text{whole}}$ ________ decimal ________

3. 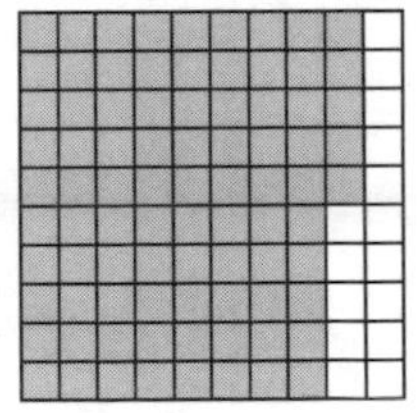

$\frac{\text{part}}{\text{whole}}$ ________ decimal ________

4. 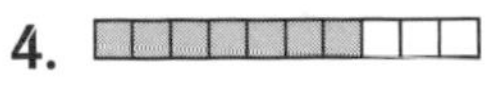

$\frac{\text{part}}{\text{whole}}$ ________ decimal ________

5. 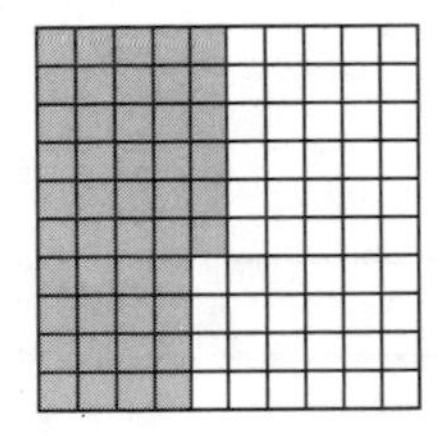

$\frac{\text{part}}{\text{whole}}$ ________ decimal ________

6.

$\frac{\text{part}}{\text{whole}}$ ________ decimal ________

7.

$\frac{\text{part}}{\text{whole}}$ ________ decimal ________

8. 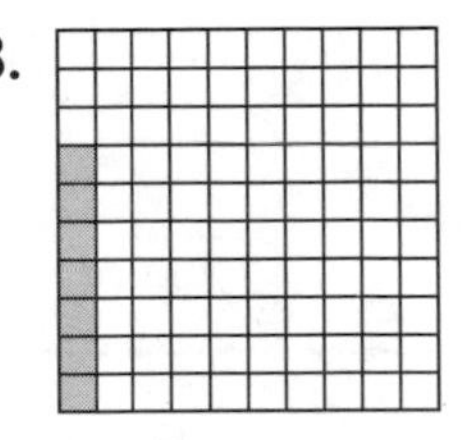

$\frac{\text{part}}{\text{whole}}$ ________ decimal ________

PCM 9

Fraction Models

Mixed Nuts

Nothing but Nuts sells specialty packages of all kinds of nuts. The nuts can be bought in different mixtures and in different size packages. The sign in the store advertises these sizes:

Nothing but Nuts

$\frac{1}{4}$ - pound bag	$1\frac{1}{4}$ - pound bag
$\frac{1}{2}$ - pound bag	$1\frac{1}{2}$ - pound bag
$\frac{3}{4}$ - pound bag	$1\frac{3}{4}$ - pound bag
1 - pound bag	2 - pound bag

Use the information above to solve each problem.

1. An employee has $6\frac{3}{4}$ pounds of pecans to package in $\frac{3}{4}$-pound bags. How many bags of pecans will there be?

2. A customer buys a $\frac{1}{2}$-pound bag of peanuts to divide among his 3 children. How much does each child get?

3. The store receives a shipment of $43\frac{3}{4}$ pounds of cashews. The manager wants this shipment to be divided into 25 bags. What size bags should be used?

4. The store receives $6\frac{1}{2}$ pounds of gourmet nuts. The manager wants to package the nuts in the smallest bags available. How many bags will there be?

5. A customer buys $8\frac{1}{4}$ pounds of nuts for a party with 44 expected guests. How many pounds of nuts are available for each guest?

6. The manager asks an employee to package 22 pounds of mixed nuts into $\frac{3}{4}$-pound bags. She wants at least 30 bags of mixed nuts. Will this work? Explain your reasoning.

PCM 11

Class Questionnaire

A. Check the appropriate box for each question.

1. I am ☐ male.
☐ female.

2. I am ☐ under 40.
☐ 40 or over.

3. I am ☐ married.
☐ not married.

4. I ☐ have children.
☐ don't have children.

5. I ☐ work outside the home.
☐ don't work outside the home.

6. I ☐ have a pet.
☐ don't have a pet.

7. I ☐ live alone.
☐ live with other people.

8. I ☐ own a car.
☐ don't own a car.

B. Use the results of the questionnaire to write the ratios described below.

1. male ______ to female ______ male ______ to total ______

2. under 40 ______ to 40 or over ______ under 40 ______ to total ______

3. married ______ to not married ______ married ______ to total ______

4. children ______ to no children ______ children ______ to total ______

5. work ______ to don't work ______ work ______ to total ______

6. pet ______ to no pet ______ pet ______ to total ______

7. alone ______ to others ______ alone ______ to total ______

8. car ______ to no car ______ car ______ to total ______

PCM 12

Percents and Vitamins

Vegetables	Serving Size (Ounces)	Percent RDA* for Vitamin A	Percent RDA* for Vitamin C
Bell Pepper	5.5	2	130
Broccoli	5.5	10	240
Carrot	3.0	330	8
Cauliflower	3.0	**	110
Cucumber	3.5	4	6
Green Bean	3.0	2	8
Iceberg Lettuce	3.0	2	4
Leaf Lettuce	3.0	20	4
Potato	5.5	**	50
Radish	3.0	**	30
Summer Squash	3.5	4	25
Sweet Corn	3.0	5	10
Sweet Potato	4.5	520	50
Tomato	5.5	20	40

* Recommended Daily Allowance
** Less than 2% RDA
Source: U.S. Department of Agriculture

1. A serving of what vegetables provides more than the recommended daily allowance of Vitamin A?

2. A serving of what vegetable provides 10% more than the recommended daily allowance of Vitamin C?

3. A serving of what vegetables provides half the recommended daily allowance of Vitamin C?

4. If you eat a serving each of sweet potato and tomato, what percent of the recommended daily allowance for Vitamin C are you missing?

5. How many servings of leaf lettuce would provide you with the recommended daily allowance for Vitamin A?

6. If you eat a salad with 3 servings of leaf lettuce, 1 serving of cucumber, 1 serving of pepper, and 1 serving of tomato, what percent of the recommended daily allowance for Vitamin A are you missing?

PCM 13

Express Yourself!

1. Approximately 85% of businesses owned by women in this country are in the retail or service industry.

Express as a ratio in lowest terms.

Answer: Approximately 17 of 20 businesses owned by women in this country are in the retail or service industry.

2. Registered Democrats make up $\frac{2}{5}$ of all registered voters in the state.

Express as a percent.

Answer: Registered Democrats make up 40% of all registered voters in the state.

3. In the average American home, about 20% of electricity used is for lighting, cooking, and appliances.

Express as a fraction.

Answer: In the average American home, about $\frac{1}{5}$ of electricity used is for lighting, cooking, and appliances.

4. Hi-Tek, Inc., reports that it will lay off 1,400 of its 4,000 employees.

Express as a percent.

Answer: Hi-Tek, Inc., reports that it will lay off 35% of its employees.

5. In a survey, $\frac{1}{3}$ of the people polled stated that the location of their workplace was the biggest factor in choosing a place to live.

Express as a percent.

Answer: In a survey, $33\frac{1}{3}\%$ of the people polled stated that the location of their workplace was the biggest factor in choosing a place to live.

6. On average, the number of beds occupied at City Hospital is 60%.

Express as a ratio in lowest terms.

Answer: On average, 3 out of 5 beds are occupied at City Hospital.

7. Experts recommend that fat in the diet be limited to no more than 30% of the total calories.

Express as a fraction.

Answer: Experts recommend that fat in the diet be limited to no more than $\frac{3}{10}$ of the total calories.

8. The player has a batting average of .250.

Express as a percent and a ratio.

Answer: The player has a batting average of 25% or 1 to 4.

PCM 14

Deal a Discount

30% OFF All Merchandise Over **$59.99**	**40% off all regular prices**	***33% off all household goods***
Clearance Sale! 50% off all items in stock	30% OFF All Items Plus Additional 10% OFF Small Appliances	LIQUIDATION SALE 75% off everything left in store
10% OFF All Items Under $50 and 20% OFF All Items $50 and Over	**20% off all health and beauty aids**	45% off entire stock of Women's Apparel and Accessories
25% off all clothing	**Price** / **Discount** up to $25.00 .... 10% $25.01 to $50 .... 20% $50.01 and over 30%	*55% OFF ALL ITEMS*

PCM 15

Speeds and Weights

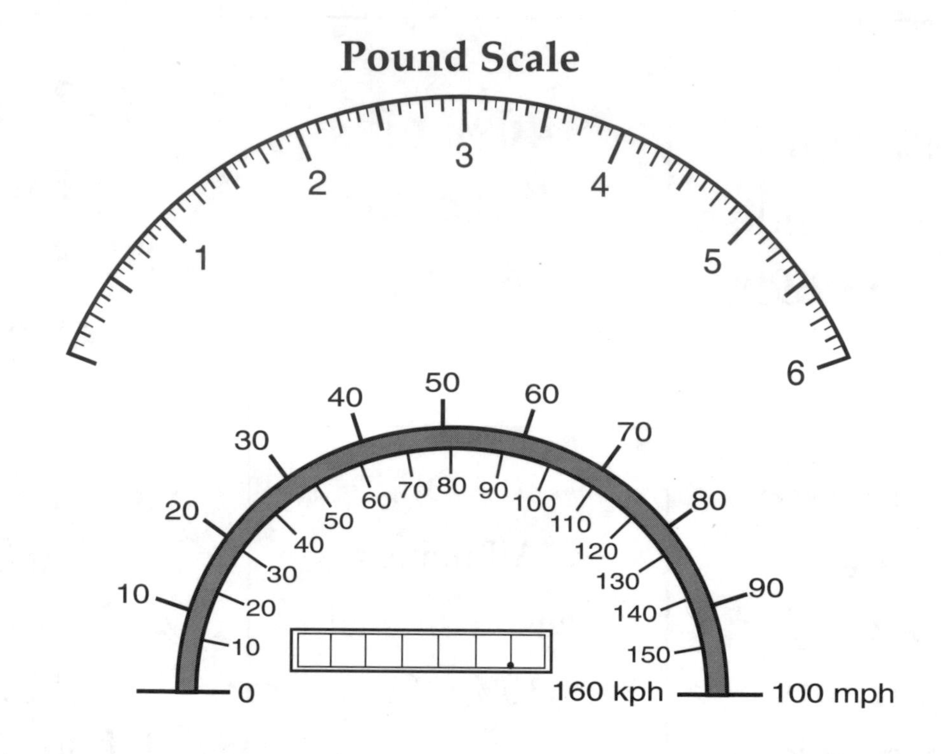

Mark the scale, speedometer, or odometer with the measures listed below. Label each point on the scale and speedometer with the matching letter.

A. A bunch of bananas weighs 4 pounds 3 ounces.

B. A car travels on the highway at a steady speed of 58 miles per hour.

C. An automobile has been driven a total of 56,975 $\frac{9}{10}$ miles. Write this distance on the odometer.

D. A bag of oranges weighs $3\frac{1}{4}$ pounds.

E. A customer weighs a bag of spinach to confirm that it contains 10 ounces.

F. A driver slows down to 22 miles per hour upon entering a school zone.

G. A car travels at 52 kilometers per hour.

H. A bunch of broccoli weighs 2 pounds 4 ounces.

PCM 16

Organize Data in a Chart

Name	Heart Rate Before Exercise		Heart Rate After Exercise		Increase in Heart Rate	
	(10 sec.)	(1 min.)	(10 sec.)	(1 min.)	(10 sec.)	(1 min.)

1. For each group member, fill in the 10 sec. columns with the heart rate information before and after exercise.

2. Multiply the 10-second rates by 6 to find the 1-minute rates. Enter these figures in the 1 min. columns.

3. Subtract to find the difference in each rate before and after exercising. Enter this information in the Increase in Heart Rate columns.

4. Analyze the data in the chart by answering the following questions:

   a. Which student had the highest heart rate before exercising? The lowest heart rate?

   b. Which student had the highest heart rate after exercising? The lowest heart rate?

   c. Discuss what factors might cause higher heart rates.

   d. How does organizing this data in a chart help you to work with the information?

Design a Spreadsheet

A. Acucorp pays its sales representatives a commission on total sales. The commission is a payment of a percentage of the representative's total sales. This partially completed spreadsheet is used to determine total commissions paid in a year.

	A	B	C	D
1	Name	Total Annual Sales	Commission Rate	
2				
3				
4				

1. Write the title for column D on the spreadsheet.
2. One representative, Richardson, has total sales of $126,200. She receives a commission of 15% of total annual sales. Write this information in row 2 of the spreadsheet.
3. What formula would you use to find the figure for cell D2 of the spreadsheet? (Think about how you calculate the percent of a number.) Do the calculation and fill in the amount of her commission in the spreadsheet.
4. Complete rows 3 and 4 using the following information:

   Cormier $168,420 at 12%

   Morelli $145,800 at 10%

   Calculate the amounts for cells D3 and D4.

B. Acucorp representatives are paid an automobile allowance for business-related travel. This rate is $.28 per mile. Design a spreadsheet to calculate this payment. Complete the spreadsheet using the following information: Richardson—894 miles, Cormier—1,090 miles, Morelli—745 miles.

PCM 18

Grid Drawings

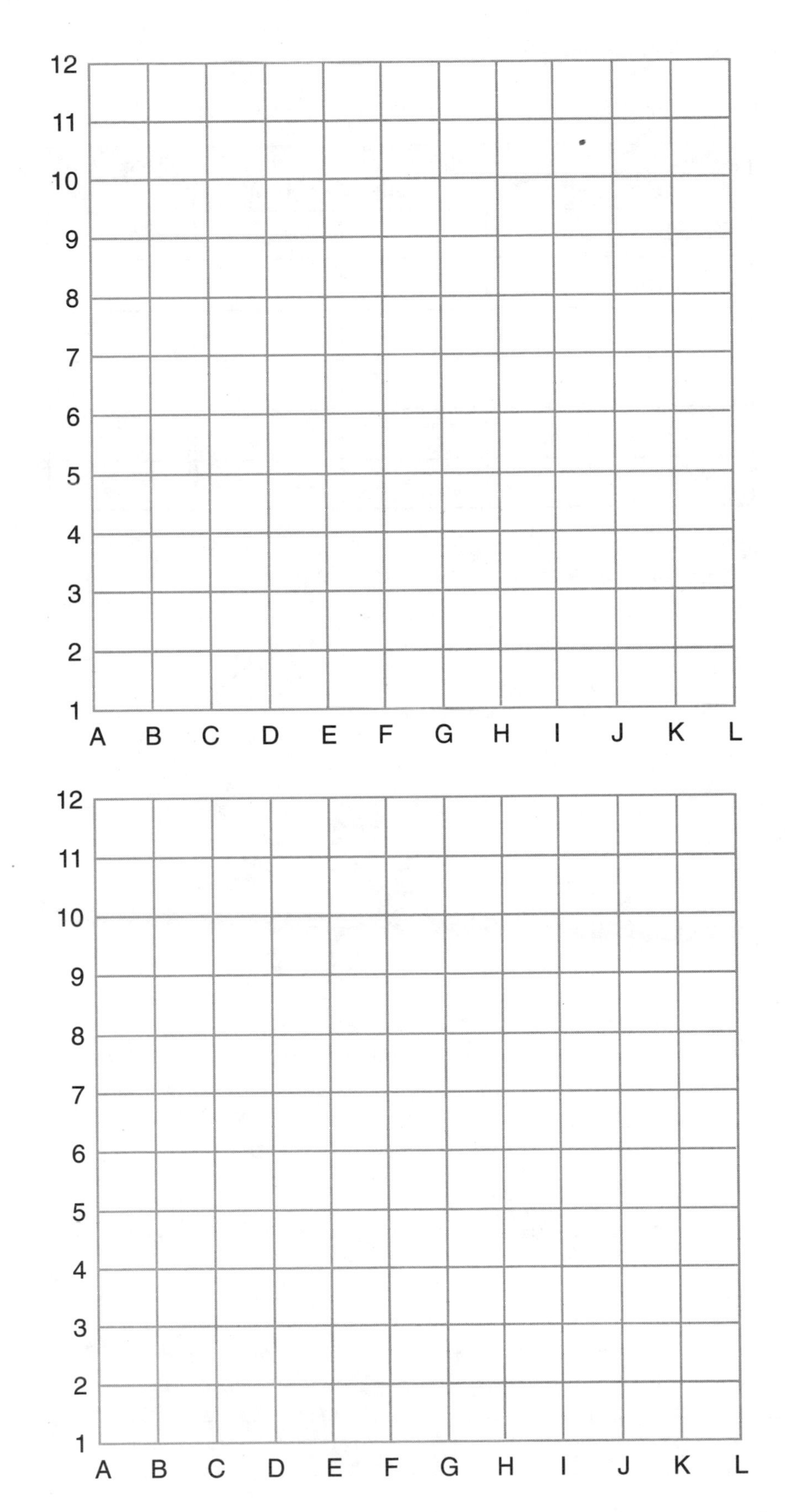

PCM 19

Dream Vacation

1. Total number of students in sample: __________

2. Use the results of the tally to complete the table.

Destination	Number of Students	Fraction of Total	Percent of Total
Beach			
Mountains			
Lake			
City			
Historical Site			
Theme Park			

3. Create a circle graph that shows the choices of the group.

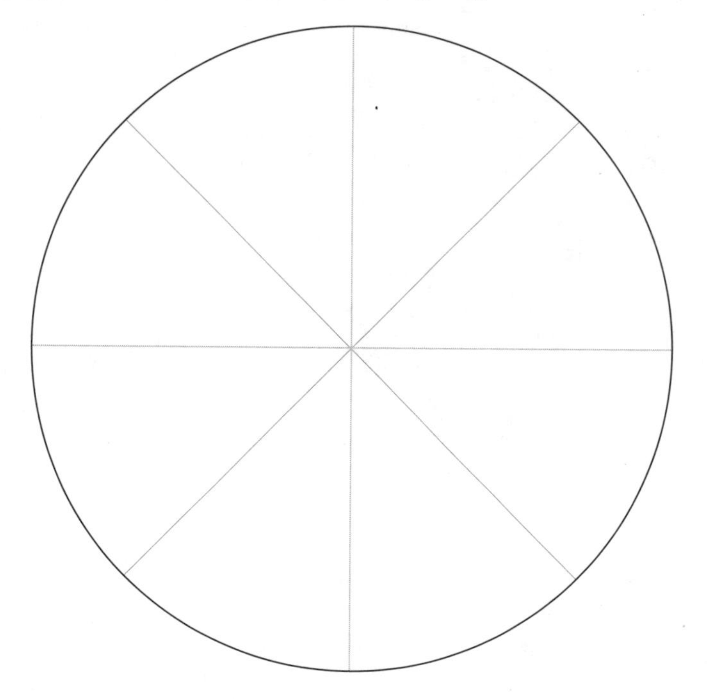

4. Write two statements that can be used to describe the circle graph you constructed.

a. ____

____

b. ____

____

PCM 20 City Data

The figures for these large U.S. cities include area and population outside of the actual city boundaries. The information includes data for continuous built-up areas surrounding the cities. Numbers have been rounded.

City and State	Land Area (sq. mi.)	1992 (estimate)	Population per Square Mile
New York, NY	1,274	14,600,000	
Los Angeles, CA	1,110	10,100,000	
Chicago, IL	762	6,500,000	
San Francisco, CA	428	4,000,000	
Philadelphia, PA	471	3,970,000	

Source: 1995 Information Please Almanac

This graph shows the approximate population per square mile for selected European cities with populations above 2 million. Numbers have been rounded.

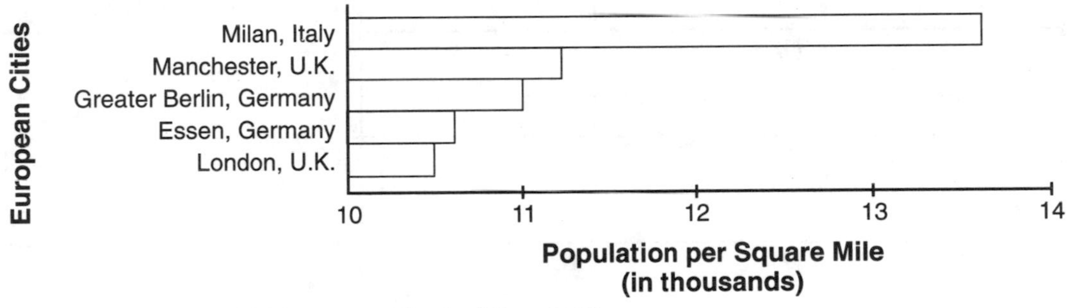

Source: The World Almanac and Book of Facts 1995

Use the data from both sources to answer the questions.

1. To find the population per square mile, divide the population figure by the number of square miles. What is the population per square mile for each of the U.S. cities? Write your answers in the table above. Round to the nearest whole number.
2. Which European city has the population per square mile closest to that of New York City?
3. The higher the population per square mile, the more densely populated the city is. Of all the cities above, which is the most densely populated? The least densely populated?
4. Based on population density, how do the U.S. cities compare with the European cities?
5. On a separate piece of graph paper, create a bar graph for the population per square mile of the five U.S. cities.

PCM 21

Testing Probability

Number of Selections

	Member	Trial 1	Trial 2
1.	______	______	______
2.	______	______	______
3.	______	______	______
4.	______	______	______
5.	______	______	______

Successive Events
Trial 1 ______

Successive Events
Trial 2 ______

Trial 1

1	2	3	4	5
6	7	8	9	10
11	12	13	14	15
16	17	18	19	20
21	22	23	24	25

Trial 2

1	2	3	4	5
6	7	8	9	10
11	12	13	14	15
16	17	18	19	20
21	22	23	24	25

PCM 22

Order the Operations

1. $3(6 + 4)^2$

   a.

   b.

   c.

2. $(2 + 6)^2 + (8 - 3)^2$

   a.

   b.

   c.

   d.

   e.

3. $\frac{60 + 15}{30 - 15}$

   a.

   b.

   c.

4. $\frac{23 + 5}{7}$

   a.

   b.

5. $\frac{\sqrt{25} + 13}{6}$

   a.

   b.

   c.

6. $3 \cdot 4 - (8 - 4)$

   a.

   b.

   c.

7. $2(5 + 6) - (5 + 7)$

   a.

   b.

   c.

   d.

8. $12 \cdot 4 - 4 \cdot 2$

   a.

   b.

   c.

9. $6 + 4 \cdot 2^3$

   a.

   b.

   c.

10. $(9 - 2)\left(\frac{14}{2}\right)$

   a.

   b.

   c.

PCM 23

Order Form

A film-developing company uses this order form for mail orders.

	Film	Number of Exposures	Number of Rolls	Cost	Total
$3\frac{1}{2}$" Prints	35 mm	12		1.50	
		20/24		2.00	
		36		3.00	
	126	12		1.00	
		20/24		2.00	
	Disc or 110	12/15		1.50	
		20/24		2.00	
				Subtotal	
				Shipping and Handling (add $.75 per roll)	
				Pretax Total	
				Sales Tax (MA and NY residents add sales tax)	
				Total Enclosed	

Use the information on the order form to write an equation for each problem. Then solve the equation to answer the question.

1. A customer from California sends several 35-mm rolls of film. The total enclosed is $12.75, and the subtotal is $9.00. How many rolls of film are enclosed?

2. A Massachusetts customer sends four 126 rolls of film, two with 24 exposures and two with 12 exposures. The total enclosed is $9.45. What is the sales tax rate?

3. An Idaho resident sends some 35-mm rolls of film to be developed. The subtotal is $9.00 and the pretax total is $12.00.

   a. How many rolls of film are included?

   b. Two of the rolls have 12 exposures. How many exposures do the other rolls have?

4. A New York resident sends $8.37 for an order. If the sales tax rate is 8%, what are the pretax total and the tax?

Landscape Design

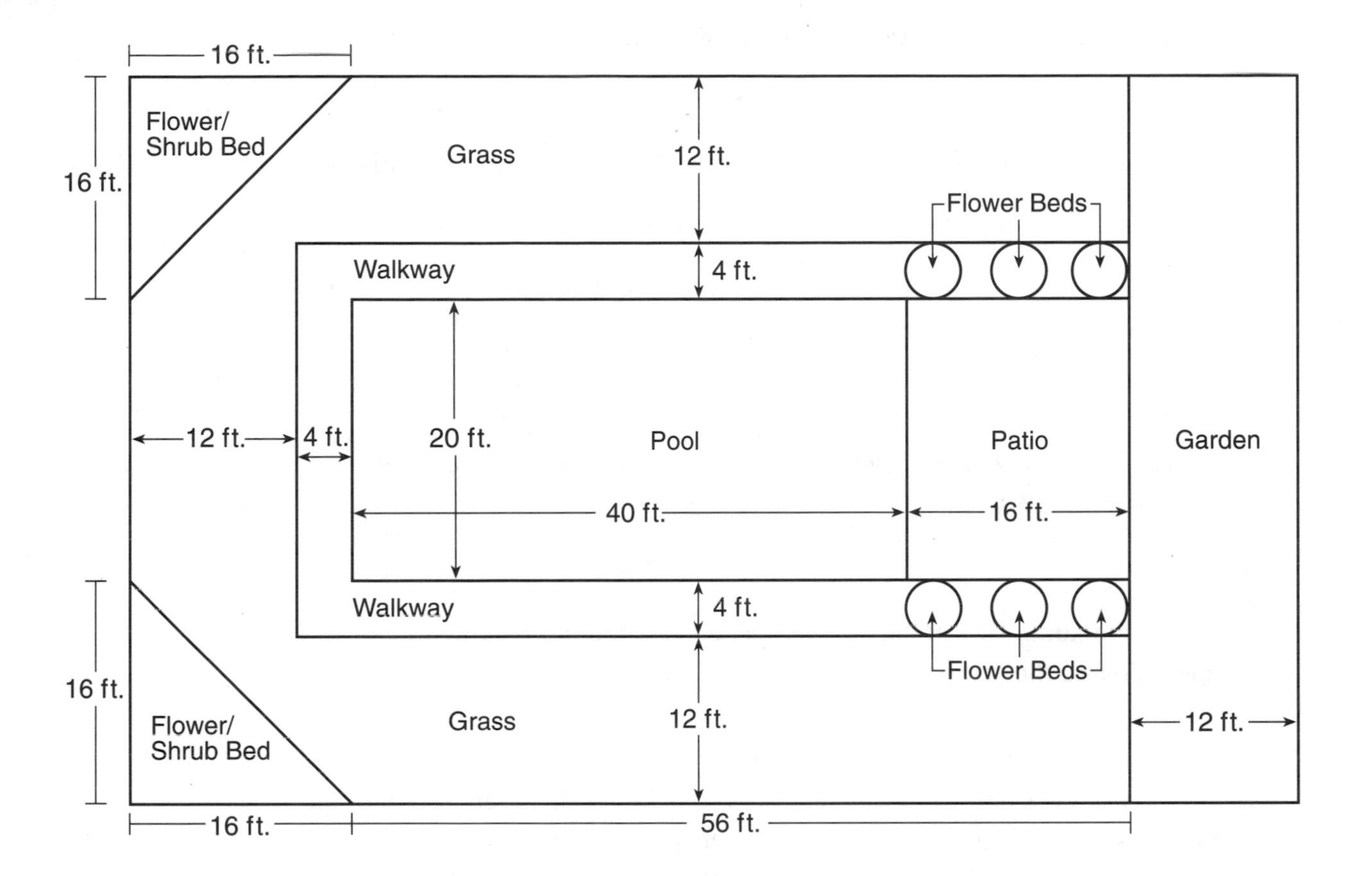

This diagram shows the plans for a pool area. Use the diagram to solve the problems.

1. The entire area will be enclosed by a fence, with one 8-foot gate. What is the total length of fencing needed (minus the gate)?

2. The circular flower beds will be surrounded by cedar edging. What length edging is needed for each bed? What is the total length needed?

3. The outside edges of the patio will consist of landscape timbers, which sell for \$1.29 per foot. What is the total length needed? What will be the cost?

4. There will be cedar edging on the front edge of the triangular flower and shrub beds. How many feet of edging are needed for both beds? (*Hint:* Use the Pythagorean theorem.)

PCM

25 Design and Area

Use the diagram on PCM 24 to answer the questions.

1. Half of the garden area will be set aside for tomato plants. What will this area be?

2. Bags of grass seed are labeled with the area in square feet that the seed will cover. What is the area in square feet to be covered by grass?

3. Tiles for the patio measure 12 inches by 12 inches. How many tiles will be needed for the patio?

4. On packages of some flower seeds, there is a measurement for the area of coverage. What is the area of coverage needed for one circular flower bed?

5. A solar cover is the same shape as the pool but is larger. It covers the pool and uses the sun's rays to warm the water. Solar covers should overhang each side of the pool by at least 1 foot. What is the smallest area that the solar cover should be?

6. What is the area of the walkway around the pool?

7. The fence that encloses the whole area is 8 feet high. Cans of paint cover a particular square-foot area. If the entire fence is to be painted, how much square footage of area must be covered? Assume the gate requires paint at the same rate as the rest of the fence. (*Hint:* Remember that both sides of the fence should be painted.)

8. In the garden, a 48-square-foot area will be used for cucumbers. What is one possible set of dimensions for this area?

Answer Key

PCM 1: Household Budgets

	Monthly	Yearly
Income:		
Take-home pay	$1,825.00	$21,900
Expenses:		
Rent	$475.00	$5,700
Utilities	160.00	1,920
Transportation	70.00	840
Telephone	40.00	480
Food	520.00	6,240
Insurance	55.00	660
Miscellaneous	190.00	2,280
Total Expenses	$1,510.00	$18,120

PCM 4: Decimal Models

1. 2.35
2. 1.25
3. 4.1
4. 10.9
5. 0.08
6. 2.8
7. 1.4
8. 8.6
9. 1.45

PCM 6: Paycheck Deductions Work Sheets

		Taxes		Other Deductions	
Gross Pay:	$320.00	Federal:	$25.59	Health Insurance:	$38.50
Less Taxes:	−57.59	State:	12.82	Life Insurance:	
Less Other Deductions:	−49.25	FICA:	19.18	Savings Plan:	10.75
Net Pay:	$213.16	Total:	$57.59	Union Dues:	
				Other:	
				Total:	$49.25

PCM 7: What Rates?

1. a. $500.00
   b. $300.00
   c. $375.00
2. a. $73.00
   b. $182.50
   c. $54.75
3. a. $980.46
   b. $1,558.68
   c. $1,194.15
4. a. 339.2 miles
   b. 254.4 miles
   c. 180.2 miles
5. a. 6.4 hours
   b. 24 hours
   c. 14.4 hours
6. a. $35,281.50
   b. $62,285.50
   c. $44,634.00
7. a. $79.50
   b. $190.80
   c. $389.55
8. a. $178.48
   b. $201.76
   c. $76.63

PCM 8: Part and Whole Models

1. $\frac{3}{10}$ 0.3
2. $\frac{24}{100}$ 0.24
3. $\frac{85}{100}$ 0.85
4. $\frac{7}{10}$ 0.7
5. $\frac{46}{100}$ 0.46
6. $\frac{5}{10}$ 0.5
7. $\frac{9}{10}$ 0.9
8. $\frac{7}{100}$ 0.07

PCM 10: Mixed Nuts

1. $6\frac{3}{4} \div \frac{3}{4} = \frac{27}{4} \div \frac{3}{4} = \frac{27}{4} \cdot \frac{4}{3} = \frac{9}{1} =$ **9 bags**
2. $\frac{1}{2} \div 3 = \frac{1}{2} \div \frac{3}{1} = \frac{1}{2} \cdot \frac{1}{3} =$ **$\frac{1}{6}$ pound**
3. $43\frac{3}{4} \div 25 = \frac{175}{4} \div \frac{25}{1} = \frac{175}{4} \cdot \frac{1}{25} = \frac{7}{4} =$ **$1\frac{3}{4}$-pound bags**
4. $6\frac{1}{2} \div \frac{1}{4} = \frac{13}{2} \div \frac{1}{4} = \frac{13}{2} \cdot \frac{4}{1} =$ **26 bags**
5. $8\frac{1}{4} \div 44 = \frac{33}{4} \div \frac{44}{1} = \frac{33}{4} \cdot \frac{1}{44} =$ **$\frac{3}{16}$ pound**
6. $22 \div \frac{3}{4} = \frac{22}{1} \div \frac{3}{4} = \frac{22}{1} \cdot \frac{4}{3} = 29.333$
   $29 \cdot \frac{3}{4} = 21.75$
   No. There is enough for twenty-nine $\frac{3}{4}$-pound bags with $\frac{1}{4}$ pound left over.

PCM 12: Percents and Vitamins

1. carrot, sweet potato
2. cauliflower
3. potato, sweet potato
4. 10%
5. 5 servings
6. 14%

PCM 15: Speeds and Weights

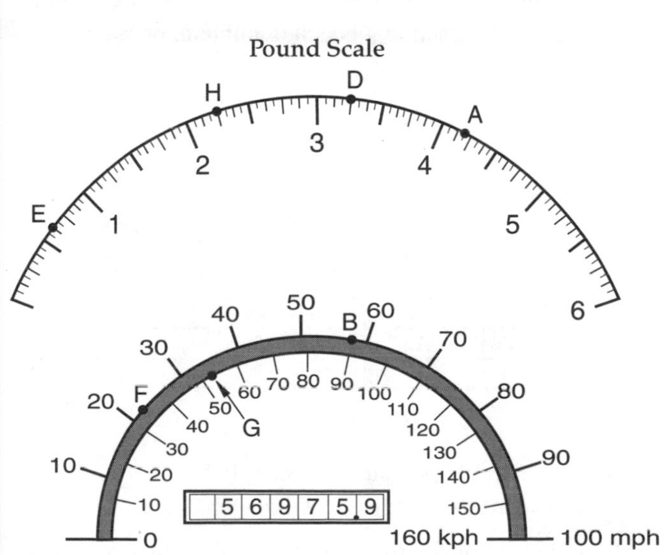

PCM 16: Organize Data in a Chart

1–3. Answers will vary.

4 a–b. Answers will vary.

c. Possible answers include exercise, exertion, conditioning, age, diet.

d. A possible answer is that organizing data in a chart makes it easier to find information and to compare data.

PCM 17: Design a Spreadsheet

Part A

	A	B	C	D
1	Name	Total Annual Sales	Commission Rate	Commission or Payment
2	Richardson	$126,200	0.15	$18,930.00
3	Cormier	$168,420	0.12	$20,210.40
4	Morelli	$145,800	0.10	$14,580.00

3. B2*C2

Part B

	A	B	C	D
1	Name	Miles	Rate Per Mile	Payment
2	Richardson	894	$.28	$250.32
3	Cormier	1,090	$.28	$305.20
4	Morelli	745	$.28	$208.60

PCM 19: Dream Vacation

4. Answers will vary. Some possible responses: Students could compare the sizes of the segments of the circle graph. They could also group segments to describe approximately half of the choices, for example, "About half the students would like to visit a natural attraction—beach, mountain, or lake."

PCM 20: City Data

1.

City and State	Land Area (sq. mi.)	1992 (estimate)	Population per Square Mile
New York, NY	1,274	14,600,000	11,460
Los Angeles, CA	1,110	10,100,000	9,099
Chicago, IL	762	6,500,000	8,530
San Francisco, CA	428	4,000,000	9,346
Philadelphia, PA	471	3,970,000	8,429

2. Manchester, U.K.
3. most densely populated: Milan, Italy
   least densely populated: Philadelphia, PA
4. In general the U.S. cities are less densely populated than the European cities.

5.

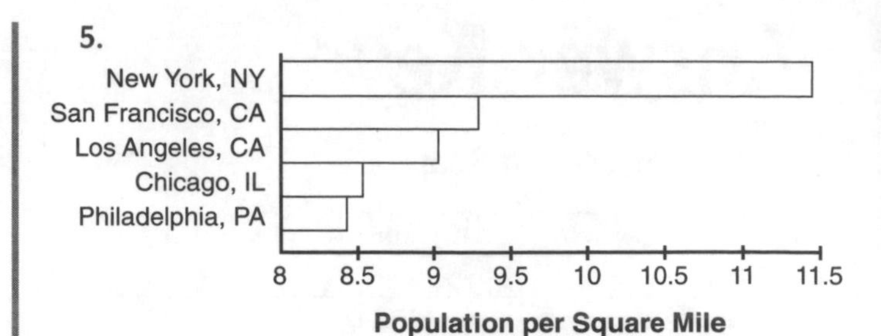

PCM 22: Order the Operations

1. a. $6 + 4 = 10$
   b. $10^2 = 100$
   c. $3 \times 100 = 300$
2. a. $2 + 6 = 8$
   b. $8 - 3 = 5$
   c. $8^2 = 64$
   d. $5^2 = 25$
   e. $64 + 25 = 89$
3. a. $60 + 15 = 75$
   b. $30 - 15 = 15$
   c. $75 \div 15 = 5$
4. a. $23 + 5 = 28$
   b. $28 \div 7 = 4$
5. a. $\sqrt{25} = 5$
   b. $5 + 13 = 18$
   c. $18 \div 6 = 3$
6. a. $8 - 4 = 4$
   b. $3 \times 4 = 12$
   c. $12 - 4 = 8$
7. a. $5 + 6 = 11$
   b. $5 + 7 = 12$
   c. $2 \times 11 = 22$
   d. $22 - 12 = 10$
8. a. $12 \times 4 = 48$
   b. $4 \times 2 = 8$
   c. $48 - 8 = 40$
9. a. $2^3 = 8$
   b. $4 \times 8 = 32$
   c. $6 + 32 = 38$
10. a. $9 - 2 = 7$
    b. $14 \div 2 = 7$
    c. $7 \times 7 = 49$

PCM 23: Order Form

1. $\$9 + \$.75x = \$12.75$
   $\$.75x = \$3.75$
   $x =$ **5 rolls of film**
2. Subtotal: $2(\$1.00) + 2(\$2.00) = \$6.00$
   Shipping and Handling: $4(\$.75) = \$3.00$
   Pretax Total: $\$6.00 + \$3.00 = \$9.00$
   $\$9 + \$9x = \$9.45$
   $\$9x = \$.45$
   $x = 0.05$, or **5% sales tax rate**
3. a. $\$9 + \$.75x = \$12$
   $\$.75x = \$3$
   $x =$ **4 rolls of film**
   b. $2(\$1.50) + 2x = \$9$
   $\$3 + 2x = \$9$
   $2x = \$6$
   $x = \$3$ (cost for each of the other two rolls)
   The other two rolls have **36 exposures.**

4. $\$1.08x = \$8.37$

   $x = \$7.75$

   The total before tax = **\$7.75;** tax = **\$.62.**

PCM 24: Landscape Design

1. length: 16 + 56 + 12 = 84 ft.

   width: 16 + 20 + 16 = 52 ft. *or*

   12 + 4 + 20 + 4 + 12 = 52 ft.

   perimeter minus gate: 2(84) + 2(52) − 8 =

   168 + 104 − 8 = **264 feet**

2. diameter of circular flower bed: 4 ft.

   $C = \pi d$ (using $\pi \approx 3.14$): (3.14)(4) = **12.56 feet**

   total edging for 6 flower beds: 6(12.56) = **75.36 feet**

3. total length of timbers needed (perimeter): 2(20) + 2(16) =

   40 + 32 = **72 feet**

   cost: 72(\$1.29) = **\$92.88**

4. $a^2 + b^2 = c^2$

   $16^2 + 16^2 = c^2$

   $512 = c^2$

   $22.63 = c$

   both beds: 2(22.63) = **45.26 feet**

PCM 25: Design and Area

1. garden area: 12(52) = 624 square feet

   half of the garden area: $\frac{1}{2}(624)$ = **312 square feet**

2. Pool and walkway are surrounded by grass on three sides.

   area of large rectangle: (56 + 16)(12) = (72)(12) = 864 square feet

   area of small rectangle: (20 + 4 + 4)(12) = (28)(12) = 336 square feet

   area of triangular flower/shrub bed: $\frac{1}{2}(16)(16)$ = 128 square feet

   grass area: 2(864) + 336 − 2(128) = 1,728 + 336 − 256 = **1,808 square feet**

3. area of patio: 16(20) = 320 square feet

   tile: 12 in. × 12 in. = 1 ft. × 1 ft. = 1 square foot

   320 sq. ft. ÷ 1 sq. ft. = **320 tiles**

4. area of circular flower bed (using $\pi \approx 3.14$): $3.14(2^2)$ = **12.56 square feet**

5. area of pool: 20(40) = 800 square feet

   area of solar pool cover: (20 + 1 + 1)(40 + 1 + 1) =

   (22)(42) = **924 square feet**

6. area of walkway: 2(4)(40) + 4(28) = 320 + 112 = **432 square feet**

7. perimeter: 168 + 104 = 272 feet

   area of fence: 8(272) = 2,176 square feet

   area of both sides of fence: 2(2,176) = **4,352 square feet**

8. Answers may vary. Some possible responses: 24 ft. × 2 ft.; 16 ft. × 3 ft.; 12 ft. × 4 ft.; 8 ft. × 6 ft.